THE OUTLAWS

THE
OUTLAWS

BY LUIGI MENEGHELLO
TRANSLATED BY RALEIGH TREVELYAN

A HELEN AND KURT WOLFF BOOK
HARCOURT, BRACE & WORLD, INC., NEW YORK

AUTHOR'S NOTE

THIS IS IN some ways a new book. The Italian original, *I piccoli maestri*, was written in the belief that, as our Duce said of his Fascism, it was not for export; and when friendly pressures in England and America persuaded me to authorize a translation, experience showed that the book could not be turned into English as it stood. So I rewrote certain passages, and cut all that seemed untranslatable—altogether more than a quarter of the original.

I should like to say to the American reader that *I piccoli maestri* (published in Italy as a novel but based on a scrupulous record of fact) was both a private "exercise in exorcism" and a public statement about the realities of the Italian Resistance. Around the *Resistenza* there has arisen a rhetorical tradition that requires, and supplies, images of conventional heroes. This I find offensive. I was there, and there were no conventional heroes. My concern was to show how much more interesting and serious it all was. The exorcism had to do with the moral shock—so many years ago—of coming to understand what Fascism was after one had been brought up as a Fascist; and with the feeling during the civil war that it would be unpardonable to survive it. When I eventually felt I had pardoned myself and my friends, in January 1963, I began to write.

READING, OCTOBER 1966

L. M.

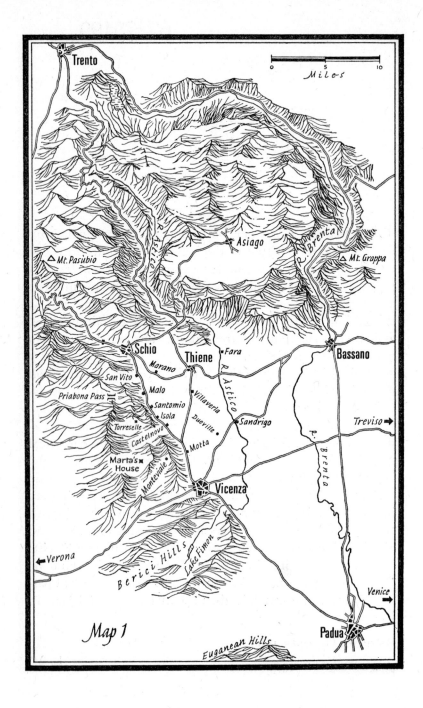

Map 1

↑
Cortina

Agordo

Miles

Map 2

Croda Grande

Pale di S. Martino

California · Canal del Mis

× Landrina

Belluno

River Piave

Northern Italy

showing areas of

Maps 1 & 2

Merano

2·Belluno

Milan ·

1

Vicenza ·

Venice

· Florence

· Tarquinia

ORome

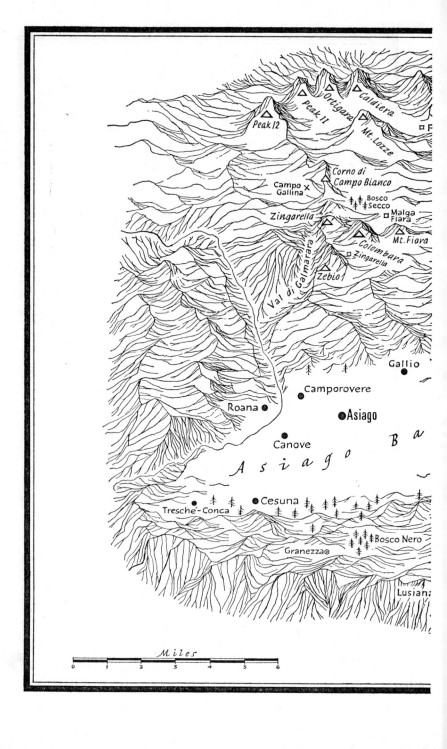

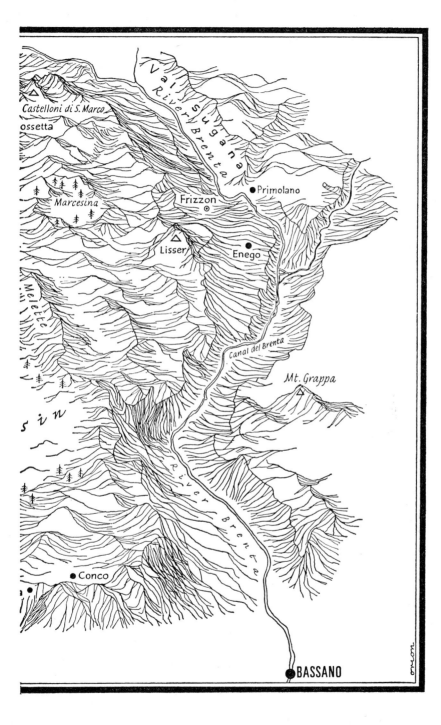

Castelloni di S. Marco

ossetta

Val Sugana
River Brenta

Marcesina

Frizzon

Primolano

Lisser

Enego

Melette

Canal del Brenta

sin

Mt. Grappa

River Brenta

Conco

BASSANO

THE OUTLAWS

1

I ENTERED the shepherd's hut and Simonetta followed; she always seemed to be following people, like a puppy. Her hair was a bit ruffled and she wasn't wearing lipstick, but she looked fresh and beautiful. The war had been over some weeks. The shepherd gave us milk out of a wooden bowl, and we drank it by turns. Then he said:

"I heard shooting."

"I came to fetch this," I said. I was carrying my sten gun over my shoulder and had tried it out in the woods. It worked perfectly.

"We're in a tent under the Colombara," I said. "We've been here three days."

He asked if we were brother and sister, and Simonetta said no. When we went outside he drew me apart and said softly: "You've got a flower." He said it as though he meant he was sorry she wasn't his flower.

We were in a little sky-blue tent. Storms came up regularly at night, and the tent would be illuminated with a

3

fluorescent glow at every flash. The light filtered in as though through a veil; so did the water for that matter. The rest of the water flowed underneath. We spent the nights seated side by side on our rucksacks, with our knees up and our arms about our legs; about our own legs, I mean—my arms about my legs and Simonetta's about hers.

I have always hated those little trenches that are supposed to be dug around tents; and in any case how on earth does one set about digging trenches on those slabs of rock below the Colombara? Anyhow it's limestone, I thought, trenches aren't necessary, limestone absorbs water. But it didn't absorb the water at all.

We climbed onto the rucksacks, so as to be out of reach of the stream, and there we stayed. The rain came down in torrents, like hail; instead of warding it off, this little blue tent seemed just to be there in order to collect it, to spill it over us. Simonetta was very sleepy: in the lightning flashes I saw her by my side with eyes closed and pouting lips; she was as wet as a rat and spiritually miles away.

Here I am with this flower, I thought, in all this uproar, on the watery fringe of the night. But strangely I did not mind: the night and the rain weren't *hostile*. A knot in my life was being untied. Yes, I thought, it doesn't matter if Simonetta is a little sleepy, if our bottoms are wet, if the stale bread (that I was chewing like mad) is soft and slimy. We could go on living like this—provided of course we have a caveful of stale bread. We are alive. I felt on the point of emerging from an enclosed world; it was one of those moments in life that happen every now and then, when a war ends, when one quarrels with one's family, or when exams are over, and one realizes that things are on the move, actually feels them move.

I felt a surge of that peculiar form of energy that we call joy. I lowered my feet into the running water, propped up Simonetta with my rucksack, so that she wouldn't topple sideways and drown in her sleep, and splashed off, sten in

hand. Outside there were some bushes of dwarf pines—
we call them *mughi*—and big lumps of rock and pines like
masts. I listened to the magnificent gunfire-crashes of
thunder; the lightning was continuous. Then I too started
to fire, and to shout, but I couldn't even hear myself in all
that noise. I sprayed the air with bullets, making little
elongated blue lights, yellow-edged; I could hardly make
out the sound of each burst, all I could hear clearly was
the snapping of the pine branches, a tiny noise isolated
from the rest.

It is a tremendous pleasure to fire away like that, on
and on. When I crawled back into the tent and propped
Simonetta against my shoulder again, she woke up and said:
"I can't even sleep with all this thunder," then she fell
asleep again immediately.

Thus for me the war ended, because it was at this very
moment that I felt it end. And so, soaking wet, with Simonetta balanced precariously beside me, I entered Peace.
Our partisan band exists no more, I thought; wars are for
partisans, peace is not.

I had come to look for this hole.

I'd looked and looked, with the somewhat passive assistance of Simonetta. For hours and hours: the area wasn't
large, but most complicated and confusing. I was all worked
up from the very beginning; every now and then I thought
we were on the right track and for a brief moment I would
think I knew my way through those deceptive knolls and
bushy hollows. Then I would get lost again.

We were both covered with sweat and dirt; by now it
was plain that it had been very silly of us even to set out
on this search for the hole. But suddenly I found it.

"We've arrived," I said to Simonetta. "It's here."

She said: "Wonderful." But I think she was beginning
to get bored. She was wearing corduroy shorts and a striped
linen blouse. We were standing there, near this hole.

It was a horizontal crack, a split in a flat piece of rock. The site was as I remembered it, only a bit more agreeable. I couldn't think of anything, I was so excited. Bees were buzzing, a thousand other creatures were flying about. It looked like any of a whole lot of cracks; nobody would ever have thought that a person could get down there, let alone two.

One had to lower oneself very, very slowly, sort of thread oneself in sideways. I knew that I would touch ground when I had my arms about three quarters outstretched, as in fact did happen. I had my eyes closed and stood there for a moment; then I opened them. I could see the roots of the *mughi*, the damp rocky walls, the dark smooth room, like an irregular cocoon flattened out at each end. Everything was still there; the book was on the ground, and when I picked it up I opened it at the spottiest page; the spots were faded, brick-colored at the edges. The sten was in its place, the barrel pointing upward, black, almost without rust; I was expecting some feeling of shock, but none came. The two magazines were on a ledge halfway up, and were dry. One was full, the other half full.

I waited a little longer, but nothing happened. I thought: It doesn't make sense; and in fact it's true, these things don't make sense. I had imagined that I had been looking for this hole, this sten, but instead it had been the sense of it all that I had been looking for; and the sense still wasn't there.

All right, I thought, during one of those *rastrellamenti* * I ended up down here; now I am here again, and there is no *rastrellamento* going on. The link between then and now exists indeed, but it's not a link that binds any more. All right, at this very spot on the earth's crust I spent the most vivid moment in my entire life. So what?

I called Simonetta and told her to come down too, and she came. First one leg reached me, then the other, solid

* *Rastrellamento*: a mopping-up operation (by the Germans).

and well made. I took both in my arms, and pulled. Soil and pebbles rained down on my face, so that I had to close my eyes again; and with my eyes closed I deposited Simonetta on the ground. Her hair was disheveled, and she wanted to tidy it, but there wasn't much room. We were standing very close, face to face, in this hole, and it was impossible to budge.

I couldn't see her very well, because the light pouring down from the opening above was almost wholly behind her, so I didn't know what sort of expression she had. Every now and then she scratched, first her bare legs, then her blouse, and I too occasionally gave myself a little scratch, because one has to scratch sometimes up there in the Altipiano,* perhaps from having to brush against dwarf pines all the time.

Here we are in this capsule, in this niche beneath the earth's surface, in a moment that is alive but without significance and which commemorates a moment and a significance that are utterly dead. We are here under the earth, which turns the opposite way to the sun, that is from my left to my right, and the other way round for Simonetta, from her right to her left. She and I are as close as two people can possibly be, almost without a single space or crevice between us, we touch everywhere; I can feel her legs, I feel all mixed up with her hair—her roots, her snail shells, her moods, if not her thoughts. We are here, stationary, yet we are turning around; we are in this instant in time, which again seems stationary but is in fact moving. Everything moves, and everything appears stationary.

Simonetta didn't speak while we stood there, nor did she for a while afterward when we climbed out again; and I didn't have anything to say either, except that after a bit I explained that these holes were called *scafe*; the rock in

* The uplands of Asiago, where much of the action of this book takes place.

the Altipiano is all made like this, I said. "It's because it's limestone," I told her. "The rock absorbs the water, and the water makes these holes."

I tried out the sten in the wood, and it worked; I showed the book to Simonetta but she wasn't very interested; then we went to the shepherd to ask for milk, because there was milk again in the huts now that the war was over; then darkness came, and we went back to our tent, and not long afterward the usual storm blew up and it started to rain and thunder.

I thought: What is private is private, and what has been has been. You can't pretend to relive the past, to reconstruct it; only a chrysalis is left in your hand. These aren't real shapes, I said to myself, this is raw material, they are just events. If there is a shape, then it must be spread over the whole story of what has been happening to us. One would have to tell this story all over again, and then perhaps the sense of the thing, if there is any, would emerge; it's certainly not here any more, not even on the highest peak, the Ortigara, or anywhere else for that matter.

All I had was this little book and this sten, like dried spores. The book made me feel neither hot nor cold (and in fact eventually I lost it again, because I'm the sort of person who loses things), but this sten gun, I thought, now that I have found it, I do want to keep it. I had others at home, in the cupboards there were more weapons than clothes, but this was not just any sten gun, it was *my* sten gun. Before I found it I was terribly afraid that on seeing it again I would be overcome with acute emotion and shame: after all, I had abandoned it right in the middle of the war. Instead, none of this happened; on the contrary. I did feel shame in general terms, because one always feels that, particularly at the end of a war in which one hasn't even died; but I also felt the first dark twinges of relief. Now it's finished, I said to myself. Ultimately it's not our fault if we are still alive. Yes, it has been a whole series of mistakes, our war; we haven't quite come up to the mark. Somehow we've managed to fail the Italian people, poor bastards, at least I certainly have. Clearly we aren't made for one another.

In the morning there was bright sunshine, and the Altipiano dried quickly. Simonetta combed herself in front of a little piece of mirror that she had; I looked at her and she made faces at me; then I looked at the little blue tent, so graceful, so serene. This is all part of Peace, I thought. Now we are in Peace.

Everything was dry, except that we had a vague sense of dampness on our bottoms. We put our bottoms in the sun to dry them, Simonetta and I, lying on our stomachs on the slabs of rock. I fitted the bullets into the magazine. I had taken them out with the excuse of wanting to count them; they were beautiful, golden, I had twenty-one.

"Twenty-one," I said to Simonetta. "Like you."

"Shall we fire them?" she said, and I said: "Let's."

We turned over, and I mounted the sten between us; she was laughing as she grasped the muzzle, I put my hands over hers and, holding them firmly, guided her finger to the trigger, and in this way we fired off the half magazine. We heard the bullets going into the sky, swift and free. I laughed as I felt the recoil, even my heart seemed to laugh. It's all over, I thought.

And when it was finally all over, I said to Simonetta: "You know, fragments from one's past don't really add up to anything. What has been has been. A vague sensation remains, such as I am feeling now."

"What sort of sensation?" she asked.

"I feel as I do when I'm at home," I said. "But more excited."

"That's because you've been brave here," said Simonetta.

"Brave?" I said. "We ran away."

"I bet you were brave."

9

"What are you talking about? Don't you see how I even abandoned the sten?"

"That's true," she said. "Why did you leave it here?"

"How should I know?" I said. "We left stens all over the place."

"Why?" asked Simonetta.

"To be perfectly honest," I said, "we weren't very good at war."

2

BUGLE CALLS. Those damned bugle calls at Merano. What the hell did they mean?

Someone had given Time a bash with a hammer, and the bits and pieces were whirling in space. Hours, days, weeks, they were all the same. This was not what one would call experience; just dehydration: everything was dry, the air, our mouths, the commands we received.

The things we had to do were meaningless. We gabbled out the Five Parts, the Eight Parts, and all the rest. Then there were obstacle courses, poles sticking up, holes in the ground, some most objectionable walls.

Lelio was with me; it was here that I met him. Though he too was from Vicenza, he had been at a different school, not at the Liceo, and I had only known him by name. We became close friends at once, and soon I came to regard him as one of that special group that ended up as a band of outlaws in the mountains. He was fair and silent, with straw-colored hair.

"You see," I would say to him, "this shows the ultimate absurdity of Italian life. If there is no meaning to what we are doing, it is because Italian life has no meaning. Otherwise this would just be routine military service."

"When all is said and done," Lelio said (he always talked like that), "we are part of this absurdity ourselves: we are right inside it."

We certainly were inside. We were enclosed by steep, glowering slopes; getting up to the top of them was an exhausting affair, weighed down as we were by heavy packs; every now and then we would be made to halt, and the sweat would quickly freeze on our faces, forming a crust of brine that veiled our eyes; then on we would go, still wearing these masks, which filtered a thin milky light. When we reached the top, we came down again, it was all climbing up to come down, coming down to climb up. Stragglers were everywhere, on the slopes, in the town, in the barracks, in the latrines.

We were the cream of Italy, not just officer cadets, but *alpini*, the elite of an elite.

There were so many bugle calls, at all hours of the day; some we understood, but what about the others?

I had a pocket Dante, and we read bits, especially the *Purgatorio*, which is about mountain climbing. It was then that I discovered how much better it is, the *Purgatorio*, than I had ever realized. I read only a few lines at a time, and the best of them I would show to Lelio. There were some really good ones; the general situation was very like ours.

"What ought we to do?" Lelio would ask me. I certainly didn't know, and when it was my turn to ask the same question, he didn't know either.

"It's like the last parody of Italian life," I said; and Lelio said: "We're right inside it."

Then came a bugle call, which also seemed to be asking questions.

"Who's a whore? Who's got clap?"

That was one of the calls we understood. "Your sister," said Lelio. He meant the bugle's. In the evening we were allowed out on a pass.

In barracks there were some real old-timers hanging about the corridors and squares. Their presence filled us with embarrassment, not to say dismay. They had nothing to do from morning until evening, these *alpini*; they stood around, sometimes singly, sometimes in groups. In theory we already knew such people existed; but to see them in the flesh was quite another thing. They had been caught by the Army three, five, nine, twelve years previously. Many had seen service in Africa, Albania, Greece, and elsewhere. Our society had sent them to all sorts of places, for reasons which they didn't even begin to care about; they had been kept prisoners like this for all those years, and there was no sign of their ever being set free. They leaned against walls and watched us being hustled by sergeants as we returned from practice and marches; when we passed they sneered at us in dialect. They were right to sneer at us, but they forgot that, before many months were up, we would be wearing our smart officers' cloaks and they would have to salute us. The coarse dialect they spoke attracted me, they were mostly from the valleys near Bergamo; but I never dared try talking to them. They played *morra* in the canteen, shouting at one another with guttural, epileptic sounds, rising occasionally to a high, unreal screech or yelp. They would pass each other a mess tin of wine—the *alpini* two-liter mess tin—and empty it every second time around.

Lelio and I used to go to the canteen and place ourselves in a corner so that we could watch them. We would suck away at our flasks, filled with a wine tasting of dirty straw, which at times we managed to make more revolting by adding some bitter fruit, bought in the canteen or stolen from orchards. The nausea we felt battled against our drunkenness. When we got back to the barrack room Lelio took my shoes off, because generally I was drunker than he was; I would feel him take off the first, though not the second, but in the morning I would find them both off all right and would put them on again, and so another day began.

Sometimes I went out on a pass, dressed up in uniform, white gloves and all, to get tight by myself. I sat down in front of the first liter of wine (there's a good wine near Merano), and drank it quickly, one glass after the other; the second liter I drank more slowly. Then with considerable caution I would return to barracks, white gloves ready under my cloak, hands ready inside white gloves, for saluting the officers—to do this one flicked back the cloak with one's elbow. Every time it happened I seemed in danger of losing my balance; but the officers noticed nothing, in fact the more zealous of them seemed to appreciate the aggressive and provocative look that all good cadets are recommended to adopt.

Then I met Beata and would spend my evenings out with her. She had red hair and would be smiling when we met, at the point where Maia Bassa ends and Merano begins. She had a pleasant jolly face, covered with freckles; she came from Lombardy but had been up there with her family for several years and spoke with traces of the local intonation, most attractively. We were always a little drunk, Beata and I, by the time my pass was over. I used to accompany her as far as the door of her house, and before leaving her I would say: "Wait before you go in," hoping she would sober up a little.

She was an ingenuous, big, kind girl. She wore shoes with low heels, and straps over the insteps. When we were out drinking, I would begin to look at her after the first glass, then I would say: "What do you represent?" and she would say: "Nothing," and I would explain that we all represent something, but the difficult part is to know what.

We just kept each other company: all I remember now is simply that I used to spend my evenings out with her up there on the northern frontier, on the roof of Italy—and that we clutched at each other lest we fall off.

> *She's been eating salad*
> *And now the poor thing must die.*
>
> *Please will you bury me*
> *Under the shadow of a pretty flower.*
>
> *And the people passing by*
> *Will say: What a pretty flower.*
>
> *It will be Rosina's flower,*
> *Rosina who died of love.*
>
> *But you don't die of love,*
> *You only die of grief.*

Giazza the orderly had a high-pitched voice, almost like a woman's. He used to sing these verses while lying on his bunk, and in between each he would wave his feet convulsively in the air and shout out a string of derisive variants of the word "Lieutenant," to mock our future rank, and indeed the whole army setup. He'd done nine years' military service.

Apple trees were in blossom on the hills around Merano; the flowering trees were like frail, luminous clouds. I won't say that this beauty annoyed us, but certainly it gave us no pleasure: it had nothing to do with us, we were absorbed by our own predicament.

We looked at the sky toward the northwest. It was pale blue, with little white clouds sailing in the spring wind. There, behind the mountain, was Switzerland; that piece of sky was Swiss sky. It seemed incredible, but we knew it was true. In a few hours, if we walked uphill, we would be out of that paralyzing stretch of land known as Italy. "Sooner or later that is just what we'll have to do," we said;

15

but then we looked around at the orderlies, the cadets, the old *alpini* lazing in the square, and any notion of deserting seemed absurd.

And so the bits and pieces continued to arrange themselves into weeks and months; in June we cadets were sent to camp in the high mountains, and immediately afterward they dispatched us to garrison a section of the Tyrrhenian coast, more or less halfway down the length of Italy, where once it had been nothing but dense undergrowth, as Dante had seen it, between Cecina and Corneto. We were in fact stationed at Corneto, or Tarquinia as it is called nowadays.

It was a strange place, Tarquinia of the Etruscans, in a strange setting. I had never thought about landscapes, except in terms of picture postcards; some pines, water and rocks, a view of a town, and in the distance, maybe, a mountain with smoke coming out of it. Or perhaps some sort of fantasy in words: *Dusk falls o'er the hills—now Italy is in azure steep'd.* The Veneto did not count; I had grown up in the midst of it, and so it had never occurred to me to call it a landscape.

At Tarquinia the landscape was indisputably, aggressively there: the effect was similar to being poleaxed. The crops had been harvested, and all we saw was wave upon wave of little bare hills, of a color something between tow and straw. It was like a desert, but an undulating one. There were some occasional spots of dark green, almost black; on arriving at one of these miniature oases we would find them composed of a few fig trees and a tomato patch or two. Sometimes we came upon them while doing tactics. We would dash along, then fling ourselves down and start crawling; one hand would be holding the rifle and the other would snatch at semiripe tomatoes. On we crawled, mouths full, eyes smarting, faces covered with dust.

The ground was dry and parched, and underfoot it seemed

hollow. In fact, every time we dug a trench—they made us dig trenches as an entertainment, not as a means of opposing Allied landings; to combat these last we had our allocation of six bullets per head—sooner or later our picks would strike a hollow space, and in a matter of moments a tomb would be exposed. We couldn't help thinking that these weren't tombs at all but subterranean refuges of a civilization that had fled from the desert above, and from the raging sun: indeed, they seemed to be the secret explanation of the whole landscape.

In the small town there were oddities too. The predominant type of young woman that we saw walking around seemed to us pure Etruscan. They had big, stumpy legs, rather attractive in an inelegant, chthonic way; legs suitable for being partly underground, with only three quarters showing above the surface. We saw these legs often in the streets; they suggested a placid, pre-Christian wantonness, without any overtones of sin. Strangely, they always seemed to appear in the same way, back-view, and fused to the women's rumps in a powerful though not especially harmonious manner; and usually on a level higher or lower than the observer, because the streets of Tarquinia either went up or down. Skirts of the period left the backs of the knees bare. The skin thus revealed had a blotchy, reddish look about it, like a sausage's. I didn't doubt for a second that Etruscan girls had been just like that. It was the first time that I found myself living in another part of Italy, and I felt those abysses of difference that one feels abroad sometimes, when the senses go off-balance, and one is seized with a slight panic at the realization that this jumble of illogicalities is usual to other people.

That was what the Etruscan girls of Tarquinia and their big legs did to me.

I kept asking Lelio: "Are these really Italians?" And he would reply: "Are we, for that matter?"

Even their wines didn't seem Italian; as we were almost

without money, we drank relatively little, but enough to make us feel ill. Only once, after having saved up for a long time, did four or five of us go to eat spaghetti in a tavern; each of us had a half-liter of this Etruscan stuff. The sad way in which we shoveled down the spaghetti seemed Etruscan to me, so did the girls who waited on us, and the wine tasted as though it had had an Etruscan spell cast over it. We all forced our faces to seem as if they were laughing, and sometimes we laughed in chorus. In a short while the rite was over; our artificial, funereal gaiety gave way to a silence drenched in melancholy. Lelio, when we left, said that he felt remorse. But it wasn't just because of being in Etruria: there was also the realization that in a poor country to eat to satiety is wrong, even if one does it only once in two months.

We were encamped on a tow-colored ridge, the Aurelia highway running not far behind us. There were a few bushes, some evil-tempered snakes, hardly any trees. The sun was vertically above us, beating down all day long in such a way as almost to stun us. Except when we had tactics, we had nothing to do from morning until evening: just like proper soldiers. Mother-naked under our *alpini* cloaks, wrapped in the cotton wool of the sun, giddy from lack of food, we wandered about the stubble. Our stomachs were yellow and swollen; we all looked as if we were pregnant. I read Seneca, the *De Ira* I think, but just for the pleasure of seeing a bit of Latin, not because of the *Ira*. It seemed the blackest moment in our lives. There were still several old *alpini* attached to us, or we to them, I forget which; these people, with their long years of military bondage, were a dumb refutation of any thought of individual rebellion.

Nearly all of us had temperatures, but it was a curious sort of malady: we did not feel feverish, on the contrary it seemed like a sedative, a sort of cold fire in the enormous heat around us.

18

certainly seemed out of place to us; however, when it came to our turn, we both took a pace forward, Lelio and I, and allowed ourselves a disciplinary embrace. He kissed me on the cheeks and called me by my name. Then he went on to the next, and I was left standing there, my face covered with his tears.

The company was disbanded with all proper ceremony. The last minutes, the last seconds, and our military service was at an end. Suddenly we found ourselves in a group of ordinary people who a moment ago had formed the company, and we were all free. The ex-officers dried their faces. The Italian Army was going home.

People were divided into those who made preparations and those who did not. We were right in the center of Italy, with four or five counties between us and home. It didn't really matter if we made preparations or not. I saw Sergeant Landolfi go off, weighed down by the regimental safe, a load fit for a mule; he had filled it with rum. He was heading for Como.

Lelio and I set off with three others, also from Vicenza; we decided to cut diagonally across Italy toward the Adriatic. We walked a long way each day. People everywhere were kind to us and gave us bread. The countryside was dusty.

When we reached Lake Bolsena we found a monastery, at the gate of which there was a nice monk who said: "Come and have supper with St. Francis," and so we went in; the supper was excellent. The monastery fascinated me: it was perfect. Big, bare, luminous corridors; light cells; the lake in front; the monks serene, kind, obviously remote from the things of this world. We spoke at length of Queen Amalasuntha, who is associated with this lake. I am sure that most of my genes intended me to be a monk; but some essential, ultimate combination was lacking, so I never did become one. The attraction of that monastery was enormous; if they

"Perhaps we'll die here," I said to Lelio, "then just as we're dead, the war will end too. When the Americans come here they'll say: 'Do you see? They've even had to call up the boys who were pregnant.' And they'll dig graves to bury us in, but when they drill into these tombs, which are there already and waiting, they'll chuck us in, so we'll become Etruscans, and that will be that." Lelio said: "Son-of-a-bitch." He didn't mean me, but the world at large.

It is strange, looking back, that I should not remember how we learned of the fall of the regime.* Military service is a powerful insulation; we were packed away with sergeants, uniforms, breechblocks, snakes; with the Etruscans and Seneca. Anything that happened outside our own little world we continued mechanically to regard as still being of supreme importance, but in point of fact it was like reading old newspapers of twenty years ago: interesting, but of course nothing to do with us. All I can say is that the end of Fascism was for me mixed up with finishing off the *De Ira*. And of course I do remember that we were knocked off-balance, disorientated.

I sincerely hope that others felt disorientated too, in Italy. However, as soon as the regime had melted away, like the top refuse on a dung-heap after a cloudburst, it became clear that the thing meant little any more; what did matter was the confusion in which we were left—the war, the allies who were enemies, the enemies who were allies.

Lelio and I went to the little library at Tarquinia to change books. There was a portrait of the King-Emperor on the wall, on its left was a portrait of D'Annunzio, on the other side was a white patch where the Duce had been. Lelio climbed on a chair, took down the King-Emperor and stood him against the wall, on the ground; then he put out

* On July 25, 1943, Mussolini had been demoted by the King and taken in custody. Marshal Badoglio was made head of the Italian government and subsequently surrendered to the Allies.

his hand to take down D'Annunzio. The librarian lady blushed violently and said: "Oh no. Please. That is D'Annunzio." Lelio said: "How right you are," and stood him against the wall next to his King. The librarian looked as though she was about to cry, and murmured: "But he's the poet of the Third Italy," or she may have said the Fourth. But we were inflexible and let both portraits have it with our boots. Then Lelio began to look at the crucifix, all on its own above the three white patches. At this the librarian went as white as the patches, but when after a while Lelio looked away from the crucifix, she turned red again and exchanged the books. All that was left was for her to turn green, to complete the colors of the Italian flag.

We heard about the armistice a few weeks later, toward evening. The announcement reached us in the form of a howl. We were sitting in front of the tents, our hands folded over our stomachs. An *alpino* ran stumbling across the camp; he was kicking at whatever came in his way, mess tins, weapons. And he was howling, like somebody half skinned alive. "It's over, it's over," we eventually understood him to be shouting. For him it was as simple as that.

The armistice is still referred to as "the 8th of September," but in effect what is meant by that occurred on the 9th or 10th, or even later. Every unit was instructed to destroy its own weapons, or make them unserviceable. Watched by sergeants, we all grasped our rifles (vintage 1891) by the barrel, chose a suitable stone, and banged them down on it as hard as we could. The butt would be damaged, but the rifle was still there, perfectly usable. So we would try again, ever more furiously, and at the same time yelling: "*Savoia!* Long live the King-Emperor!" We stood in a circle, banging away, on and on. We felt it was all wrong, but the satisfaction was enormous.

That was our most deeply felt half hour of the war. I think that even the most patriotic of Italians ought to be grateful to us for our part in hastening the moderniza-

20

tion of the country's military equipment. And yet not help feeling sorry for our venerable 1891 blun we had not appreciated how good they were, our grandfathers had fashioned them; and only we realizing this, now that we had to destroy found the act so hard.

After we had smashed our personal weapons, I wandered among the tents in a daze, and started the undamaged rifles and cases of ammunitio about all over the place; then we would pick so not knowing what to do with them, would fling again. Nearby there was a tomb we had recently "Let's give these things to the Etruscans," said I we did; after all, they were virtually contemporari

At the last minute we decided to keep a r well as some magazines; we took them almost th inertia, because there were so many of them, we knew what lay ahead. It was going to be road; we did not even know that there was g road at all; we felt as if we were in a circus dressed up as *alpini*.

Our Captain formed up the company, wept then embraced us one by one.

"Why are they weeping?" whispered Lelio.

I suggested that perhaps it was an old mil but Lelio screwed up his face at this. I don were worried about losing their jobs, they wer ing some general patriotic distress. They cri poor things: I was surprised and a little in Captain had a glass eye and for a momen whether he was crying with that too, but I see. He was a small, pleasant man: I have si that later he was killed during the civil war on the wrong side, and for that I am sincer patriotic distress of his on the 8th (or 10th)

"Perhaps we'll die here," I said to Lelio, "then just as we're dead, the war will end too. When the Americans come here they'll say: 'Do you see? They've even had to call up the boys who were pregnant.' And they'll dig graves to bury us in, but when they drill into these tombs, which are there already and waiting, they'll chuck us in, so we'll become Etruscans, and that will be that." Lelio said: "Son-of-a-bitch." He didn't mean me, but the world at large.

It is strange, looking back, that I should not remember how we learned of the fall of the regime.* Military service is a powerful insulation; we were packed away with sergeants, uniforms, breechblocks, snakes; with the Etruscans and Seneca. Anything that happened outside our own little world we continued mechanically to regard as still being of supreme importance, but in point of fact it was like reading old newspapers of twenty years ago: interesting, but of course nothing to do with us. All I can say is that the end of Fascism was for me mixed up with finishing off the *De Ira*. And of course I do remember that we were knocked off-balance, disorientated.

I sincerely hope that others felt disorientated too, in Italy. However, as soon as the regime had melted away, like the top refuse on a dung-heap after a cloudburst, it became clear that the thing meant little any more; what did matter was the confusion in which we were left—the war, the allies who were enemies, the enemies who were allies.

Lelio and I went to the little library at Tarquinia to change books. There was a portrait of the King-Emperor on the wall, on its left was a portrait of D'Annunzio, on the other side was a white patch where the Duce had been. Lelio climbed on a chair, took down the King-Emperor and stood him against the wall, on the ground; then he put out

* On July 25, 1943, Mussolini had been demoted by the King and taken in custody. Marshal Badoglio was made head of the Italian government and subsequently surrendered to the Allies.

19

his hand to take down D'Annunzio. The librarian lady blushed violently and said: "Oh no. Please. That is D'Annunzio." Lelio said: "How right you are," and stood him against the wall next to his King. The librarian looked as though she was about to cry, and murmured: "But he's the poet of the Third Italy," or she may have said the Fourth. But we were inflexible and let both portraits have it with our boots. Then Lelio began to look at the crucifix, all on its own above the three white patches. At this the librarian went as white as the patches, but when after a while Lelio looked away from the crucifix, she turned red again and exchanged the books. All that was left was for her to turn green, to complete the colors of the Italian flag.

We heard about the armistice a few weeks later, toward evening. The announcement reached us in the form of a howl. We were sitting in front of the tents, our hands folded over our stomachs. An *alpino* ran stumbling across the camp; he was kicking at whatever came in his way, mess tins, weapons. And he was howling, like somebody half skinned alive. "It's over, it's over," we eventually understood him to be shouting. For him it was as simple as that.

The armistice is still referred to as "the 8th of September," but in effect what is meant by that occurred on the 9th or 10th, or even later. Every unit was instructed to destroy its own weapons, or make them unserviceable. Watched by sergeants, we all grasped our rifles (vintage 1891) by the barrel, chose a suitable stone, and banged them down on it as hard as we could. The butt would be damaged, but the rifle was still there, perfectly usable. So we would try again, ever more furiously, and at the same time yelling: "*Savoia!* Long live the King-Emperor!" We stood in a circle, banging away, on and on. We felt it was all wrong, but the satisfaction was enormous.

That was our most deeply felt half hour of the war. I think that even the most patriotic of Italians ought to be grateful to us for our part in hastening the modernization of the country's military equipment. And yet we could not help feeling sorry for our venerable 1891 blunderbusses; we had not appreciated how good they were, how well our grandfathers had fashioned them; and only now were we realizing this, now that we had to destroy them, and found the act so hard.

After we had smashed our personal weapons, Lelio and I wandered among the tents in a daze, and started to pile up the undamaged rifles and cases of ammunition, scattered about all over the place; then we would pick some up but, not knowing what to do with them, would fling them down again. Nearby there was a tomb we had recently uncovered. "Let's give these things to the Etruscans," said Lelio, and so we did; after all, they were virtually contemporaries.

At the last minute we decided to keep a rifle each, as well as some magazines; we took them almost through sheer inertia, because there were so many of them, not because we knew what lay ahead. It was going to be a very long road; we did not even know that there was going to be a road at all; we felt as if we were in a circus, like clowns dressed up as *alpini*.

Our Captain formed up the company, wept as he spoke, then embraced us one by one.

"Why are they weeping?" whispered Lelio.

I suggested that perhaps it was an old military custom, but Lelio screwed up his face at this. I don't think they were worried about losing their jobs, they were just expressing some general patriotic distress. They cried like calves, poor things: I was surprised and a little impressed. Our Captain had a glass eye and for a moment I wondered whether he was crying with that too, but I couldn't quite see. He was a small, pleasant man: I have since found out that later he was killed during the civil war, and of course on the wrong side, and for that I am sincerely sorry. That patriotic distress of his on the 8th (or 10th) of September certainly seemed out of place to us; however, when it came to our turn, we both took a pace forward, Lelio and I, and allowed ourselves a disciplinary embrace. He kissed me on the cheeks and called me by my name. Then he went on to the next, and I was left standing there, my face covered with his tears.

The company was disbanded with all proper ceremony. The last minutes, the last seconds, and our military service was at an end. Suddenly we found ourselves in a group of ordinary people who a moment ago had formed the company, and we were all free. The ex-officers dried their faces. The Italian Army was going home.

People were divided into those who made preparations and those who did not. We were right in the center of Italy, with four or five counties between us and home. It didn't really matter if we made preparations or not. I saw Sergeant Landolfi go off, weighed down by the regimental safe, a load fit for a mule; he had filled it with rum. He was heading for Como.

Lelio and I set off with three others, also from Vicenza; we decided to cut diagonally across Italy toward the Adriatic. We walked a long way each day. People everywhere were kind to us and gave us bread. The countryside was dusty.

When we reached Lake Bolsena we found a monastery, at the gate of which there was a nice monk who said: "Come and have supper with St. Francis," and so we went in; the supper was excellent. The monastery fascinated me: it was perfect. Big, bare, luminous corridors; light cells; the lake in front; the monks serene, kind, obviously remote from the things of this world. We spoke at length of Queen Amalasuntha, who is associated with this lake. I am sure that most of my genes intended me to be a monk; but some essential, ultimate combination was lacking, so I never did become one. The attraction of that monastery was enormous; if they take in unbelievers, I thought, I might almost come here when peace is declared.

We entered Umbria and noticed that it was not green, as it is in poetry. We fired at crows, though with little chance of hitting them with single bullets. This is the last thing I remember about my rifle: firing at those crows, on the cigar-colored meadows of Umbria, and how they flew off at the sound of the shot, not through necessity but through prudence. I do know that when I reached home I didn't have my rifle with me any more, and this was the first rifle I lost during the war.

They were quite a sight, the roads in Central Italy at that period; there were two lines of people, one lot going north, another going south, all quite young, many in peculiar uniforms, many in oddments of civilian clothes—women's blouses, sandals, football boots. Several were dressed as priests. There was an extraordinary assortment of conveyances too: donkey-carts, hand-carts, milk-carts, wheelbarrows, bicycles with and without a chain.

The two columns waved gaily at one another. On one side of the road you heard the Venetian, Piedmontese, or Bergamasque dialects, on the other dialects from the south. It seemed that the youth of Italy, or rather the young males, had decided to swap places en masse, a sort of huge pilgrimage in fancy dress. Just look, I thought; all Europe is grimly engaged in making war, and our people improvise this festival. Undoubtedly we are a resourceful people.

We were walking in the late afternoon, with the sun behind us, when a kind of golden mirage appeared to the east and Lelio told me that it was Orvieto. It really was a spectacle.

We walked on a little, looking at this golden mirage, and then I said to Lelio:

"Is Orvieto the capital of a province?"

Lelio thought it wasn't.

"What province is it in, then?" I asked.

"How should I know?" said Lelio. "Perugia, I suppose."

"And who do you think is in command at Perugia itself?" I said.

"Search me," said Lelio.

"It's all very peculiar. I wonder who on earth runs the country now."

We waited for the others, who were a little way behind, then started to walk on into the violet dust in which the apparition of Orvieto floated.

We passed through a hamlet. A peasant seated in a doorway called to us: "Hey, *alpini*." We went up to him, and he said: "There are Germans around that corner. They are disarming soldiers."

Germans, I thought; how do Germans come into this? Bastards. By that time I had lost my rifle, so I was already disarmed; my companions, however, still had theirs. The peasant said: "I'll take your rifles if you like. I'll look after them for you"; and my companions gave them to him.

We went around the corner but found no Germans. A little man, aged about thirty-five and bareheaded, was standing there with his back to Orvieto and with his hands in his pockets. As we passed we said good evening to him. "Halt," he said. He was the Germans.

"Are you armed?" said this little man in his own language.

I wanted to show off by answering him in his language too, but there was no time because he had come up to me and had already begun feeling my thighs. Then he did the same to each of the others.

Finally I thought of something. "Are you looking for weapons, or ammunition as well?" I asked him. My accent wasn't bad, though a shade rasping. All the same he did not reply. Now we saw that, behind a tuft of bushes, there were other, younger men, looking like his assistants and engaged in loading rifles onto a truck. In my trouser pocket I had a bullet, not a whole one, but only the little lead cylinder part.

If ever I find one of these things, I always have to pick it up. I remember finding one on the shingle bed of the Piave when I was a child. It was the first time I had seen the Piave.* I went down onto the shingle by the bridge with enormous emotion and there on the sacred shingle, my Eldorado, I found a bullet. I grasped it fervently, and asked myself: Has it killed an Italian or a German? It never occurred to me that the opposing armies, both entirely composed of heroes, could have wasted a single shot. But soon I realized that this undoubtedly homicidal bullet was on the wrong side of the Piave to have killed a German. This piece of deduction made me tremble. Wars are very attractive things, especially in films, silent ones: soldiers mass, dash about; everyone is brave; a piano plays stirring tunes; bayonets gleam; people are tripping and falling all the time; they are the Fallen. There is no noise and no pain is involved. But there, on the real shingle of the Piave, with this real bullet, this hard oblong thing, in my hand, I was assailed by the idea that when it passed through your body it did cause pain, and you died of it. Has it killed a man? I asked myself. I was wearing a smart, buttoned-up jacket and patent-leather shoes.

So now I went up to the German with my fist clenched; then I opened it suddenly as though to give him a surprise. "Do you call this ammunition?" I said. "Tell me now, frankly." But he said nothing; he wasn't even annoyed, only preoccupied and in a hurry. Bastards. We went away. Our companions started to talk:

"If we had had our rifles he would have disarmed us."

"Why do they want our rifles? Haven't they got enough already?"

It was at this point that I realized who was in command now. I must have been one of the stupidest Italians alive.

* The river Piave, scene of battles 1917–18, when it became the line of defense the Austrians were unable to cross, hence the "sacred river" of the Great War.

If I had thought of this half an hour before, very probably—with the temperament I have—someone would have ended up as the first victim of the Resistance in Umbria.

On entering Orvieto we saw on a wall a poster, new, white, sinister. I don't remember who had signed it, or what it said precisely. It contained injunctions, exhortations, and threats in the name of both the Fatherland and our ally. Immediately I felt a great sense of relief, and saw everything perfectly in perspective. At long last the time to rebel had come. I said to Lelio: "What do you think?" He was staring at the poster. "Christ!" he said and I took it to mean that his thoughts were running on the same lines as mine. Our companions didn't speak. One finished up by joining the Fascist Black Brigades,* perhaps because he was attracted by the flashy uniform; the others made sure that at the end of the war they had some modest association with the winning side.

There is a railway station at Orvieto; and so after some wangling, with the unconditional approval and support of the Italian people, and with our *alpini* hats sometimes on our heads, sometimes in our pockets, we went home. And every now and then, as we dodged Germans and dashed in and out of stations and trains, we would think to ourselves: Christ!

* An auxiliary corps of the Fascist Party's Black Shirts, composed of so-called action squads and set up to combat the partisans.

3

"*Alpini,* QUICK! This way, that way!" The people of Italy
seemed determined to protect their Army, seeing that it had
proved itself incapable of looking after itself; they wouldn't
hear of anyone taking it away from them. When we reached
the station at Vicenza we were seized and virtually passed
from hand to hand until we got to safety. The women appeared to want to cover us up with their skirts: some of them
actually tried to do so.

Lelio went home, I set off for my *paese*.* "There is a
Steyr pistol at my house," I told him. "Come up when you're
ready, and we'll try it." As soon as I got home, I was given
a zabaglione; it was delicious. The Steyr was in the top
drawer of the chest in my father's room; there were about a
dozen bullets too. When Lelio arrived on his bicycle from
Vicenza, we went into the orchard to try it out.

From the scrap-heap I took an old piston, about the size

* *Paese* to an Italian means something between a village and a small
town.

of a human heart, put it on the wall, and fired twice: one miss and one hit. The piston was shattered to bits. "Now you try," I said to Lelio; I chose a big ripe tomato and put it on the wall; when he fired, it did not move but instead I saw that it was slowly bleeding; the shot had gone straight through. During the time we were cadets we had been trained to shoot with every sort of weapon apart from the pistol. "We know now that we've got the knack," I said; and from then onward throughout the war I did not have to bother about my aim.

And so, with this newly acquired confidence, and with the Steyr in my pocket, we went up Monte Pian to find a suitable place. Suitable for what? All was still vague.

Lelio and I had more or less assumed that we would have to be rebels on our own, just the two of us against the people who were issuing the posters; we had not seriously considered whether anybody else would be likely to be interested. We were in for a shock. My *paese* was full of men who felt exactly like ourselves; soldiers kept arriving from the four corners of the horizon, and all were looking for one another, looking for us, wanting to do something, to get organized.

We called a meeting in the open air among the trees at La Fontanella behind the sanctuary of Santa Libera; to this spot there came, one might say, all the youth of the neighborhood, from those who had not yet been called up to the hoariest, most venerable individuals who had left ten, eleven, twelve years before and were now back, indeed prepared to associate with us. I was filled with a kind of manic euphoria, I itched to begin, to get moving. We had all sorts, *popolani* and middle class, soldiers and civilians, schoolboys, men who had been rejected at their army medicals, tradesmen, churchgoers, thieves, schoolmasters, even a few cripples: all sorts.

I was rather ashamed to find myself talking too much as though I were lecturing, and that everybody listened to me; I spoke rapidly and fluently, as from a printed book. It would be best to burn all printed books and start again, I thought; and if we students have learned some of them by heart then these people would do well to burn us too (though I didn't actually say this to the others). The fact was it made me uncomfortable to see that I was judged capable of commanding because I happened to be able to speak well. Speaking came easily to me; I had only got to open my mouth, and out would pour ideas, projects, plans, and once they were out they seemed authoritative. A humanist education is a great advantage: he who speaks, other things being equal, is the boss.

But I had a special grudge against this humanist education: it had played me some dirty tricks. So I did not want to command. All the same I spoke. I said: "Don't let yourselves be influenced by anybody, least of all by me; you must do only what seems right to you," and everybody said: "My God, he's right; let's do as he says."

However, even though I did speak, it didn't silence the others. They just spoke rather less frequently and less flamboyantly. Everybody had his say, we felt we were in agreement.

Rino was sitting on the ground next to me while we argued about how to steal certain pistols. He pulled up a trouser leg and put a finger in his sock. "The best weapon of all is this," he said. He drew out a long, cylindrical, very sharp file, a sort of awl, but as thin as a thread. He kept it point downward in his sock. It made me think of Luccheni, the anarchist who stabbed, or should we say pricked, Elisabeth of Austria, wife of Franz Josef, with a similar blade, so sharp and thin that she never realized what had happened to her; there she stood, talking in her sad, absent-minded way, and all the time she had this blade literally threaded through her heart, and nobody knew until she collapsed and died.

I felt various currents flowing together, up at La Fontanella: the tradition of political anarchy, the tradition of chicken stealing, Crocean historicism, anti-Fascism. One

was conscious of witnessing a very singular process, something to do with the underlying components of Italian life,
of European history even. That day I went home humming:

> Old Ceco-Bepe *
> Was very coarse.
> He beat his wife
> As he hadn't a horse.

Historically this was not true; Franz Josef was extremely
distinguished, his wife even more so, though she was also a
bit mad. Rino offered to make me a similar dagger, and I
agreed. I was rather embarrassed, I must admit. When eventually he gave it to me, I felt very uncomfortable, it reminded me rather too much of stabbings in tavern quarrels.
If things go on like this, I thought, they'll soon be giving
me an instrument for picking locks. What was more, this
blade was very difficult to keep upright in one's sock; either
I didn't put it in far enough and it kept working its way
out, or I stuck it in too far and it jabbed my ankle. My sock
became a mass of holes. This is nice, I thought in the midst
of these technical difficulties; one can't tell whether it's Rino
joining me, or I him.

Actually it was all great fun. The students and the *popolani* took the lead over the others; their incredible alliance
came about quite naturally. All the same the others were
busy too, everyone wanted to do something, even the smart
young playboys from the piazza—it was they who put themselves in charge of cutting off the hair of the girls who had
been seen with Germans (though admittedly not for political reasons, poor creatures). The executioner was the principal hairdresser in town, so the cut was well, almost elegantly, done.

I cordially envied the assistants who went off so cheerfully
and in such a sporting mood to hold the girls; to be able

* Franz Josef.

30

to hold a girl really tight! And the tighter you held her, the more patriotic you were. They left on bicycles, toward evening, for the various towns in the Alto Vicentino. The hairdresser would be in the midst of them; he was a smooth, polite person, and his bag of instruments would be with him. I never went, out of a sense of discipline.

One man, still quite young, wore black boots, a curious fur cap, and two long, glossy, thick whiskers. He had the velvety eyes, the manners, and all the splendor of the gypsy. We would plan out this or that enterprise, calculate the risks; but when we had to choose someone to go through with the thing, it was always he who lifted his hand and said: "I'll do it." And he always did go, either alone or with others (as you say in confession *), on foot or on a bicycle, to fetch weapons or disarm people. This he did as easily as anybody else would breathe. He would turn up with a big haversack on his back, or pushing a barrow, or with a pedal cart, laden with the damp explosives, the crotchety old pistols and leprous-looking bayonets in which we dealt at that time.

His name was already a legend: he came from a family that had always carried on a sticky and tempestuous relationship with the *carabinieri*. Instead of being alarmed I was excited by this; we are dismantling a society, I thought, so why not? In our group we also had a couple of ex-*carabinieri*; and it was curious to see them together out on a raid, the man in the fur cap and his hereditary enemies, intent on some patriotic theft. His subsequent career was brilliant, he was a natural leader, and the civil war that later on was waged on our hills is associated with his name. It is a great honor for us students to have been with him at the time of these obscure beginnings.

Italian society, however, was not dismantled. After the

* Confessor: "Have you committed impure acts?" Penitent: "Yes." Confessor: *"Da solo o con altri?*—Alone or with others?"

war the man in the fur cap soon went back to prison, and I say this is a shameful thing to have happened.

I soon got in touch with my friends at Vicenza and introduced Lelio to them; the group of my friends, I should say, because we regarded ourselves as a group; we were mostly school friends, we had been at the Liceo or were at the University together; our bond was not just one of comradeship but that of a common education, such as school or University certainly did not provide. But we had been exposed to a different kind of schooling, with quite other teachers.

I used to explain this to Lelio during the months of our military exile, on our cadet course. "There's no Italy left," I would say to him, "nothing that can decently be called Italian—apart from the thoughts and feelings of those who are total opponents of the regime, those who reject everything and will not compromise; like Antonio Giuriolo, for example. He is from Vicenza, aged about thirty; he's a teacher but he doesn't teach because he refused to join the party."

"I thought there weren't people like that any more," said Lelio.

"Well, he's one," I said. "And my friends and I are in effect his disciples."

"Did you say disciples?" asked Lelio, who was suspicious of such words. But I explained that if you got to know Toni Giuriolo at all well, you inevitably became his disciple. And this also happened if you got to know one of his existing disciples. "You see, you are a disciple yourself now," I said.

"How many of these disciples are there, then?"

"About a dozen of us."

"Like J. Christ's."

"Those were Apostles."

I took the opportunity of giving him a brief bibliography on the Apostles: Omodeo, Renan, historical criticism. Lelio was impressed. "How on earth do you know these things?"

"Giuriolo teaches what they ought to have taught us at school."

Lelio asked me what the Apostles had to do with Italy, and I said they had a lot to do with it, though I couldn't explain why. I think I vaguely felt that having a *patria*, belonging to a country, must have to do with possessing a set of ideas, a cultural tradition—and that means knowing about things that are worth knowing, including the Apostles, or modern poetry, or anything else that seems important enough.

"Unfortunately it may be too late for us personally to learn and unlearn enough," I said to Lelio, and he said: "How cheerful can you be."

During my months in the Army I'd partly lost touch with these friends—just a cryptic postcard every now and then. Now we got together again, though there were difficulties. Antonio Giuriolo was away from the area; after the armistice and the end of Badoglio's forty-five days,* he could hardly afford to be seen in Vicenza, where he would be arrested on sight. We heard he had joined some units that called themselves partisans near the Yugoslav border. It all seemed very Slav; admirable but somewhat foreign, barbarian. One or two of the others were out of action, too, again on account of their activities during the forty-five days. Franco was in prison at Verona (he came out a few months later, but he was still there when Ciano was tried and shot: they didn't know how much more dangerous Franco was than poor Ciano). So we were rather leaderless at the moment, and each of us had independently become involved in some local Resistance activity at Vicenza or in the district. Yet we very strongly felt that we wanted to act as a group—we meant to make ourselves into a compact little team, a squad of perfectionists from Vicenza: Bene, Bruno, Nello, Lelio,

* July 25–September 8, 1943. On September 8, Badoglio surrendered to the Allies. The Germans thereupon liberated Mussolini, reinstated a Fascist government, and the war was continued.

Mario, Enrico, myself, and one or two others. After our main activities during the hours of daylight, we began to hold special meetings "overtime," in the evenings. We discussed how we could obtain personal weapons. "It's a small job," I said, "but a beginning." We went over suitable methods at enormous length; our bourgeois upbringing was a big hindrance: we were tough and merciless in theory, but in practice scrupulous and sensitive.

If what you want is the annihilation, pure and simple, of your subject, then any method you may choose is all right, and the hatchet is the easiest, but if you only want to take away a chap's pistol, then you have got to think of a subtler method—even a bang on the head with the flat side of a hatchet is a bit uncouth. So we went to a pile of firewood and chose some cylindrical stakes, of suitable dimensions: about an inch and a half in diameter and about sixteen inches long. These seemed to be the ideal instruments; but then a thought struck us: Doesn't everything depend on how *hard* you deliver the blow? With some regret, therefore, we wound cloths around the stakes, to make the things less lethal.

And so, when evening came, we used to wander around the streets of Vicenza in patrols of three. We wore raincoats and had our hands in our pockets; the one in the middle carried the stake. We would choose an officer with great care and start following him. But some of the officers would persist in walking among the crowds in the Corso, where the approach was practically impossible. Others did turn into side streets, but far too quickly so that to catch up with them we had to break into a run, and they would turn around to see what on earth was going on; then we would have to slow up and saunter by, pretending we had been running on some business of our own. Many a time we got ourselves almost within striking distance of our quarry's head—almost, but not quite. On some occasions the stake was actually raised, but no more than raised. It's not so simple to strike a moving target. We decided to separate; one of us would go ahead and stop the officer, asking for a light, then the other two could creep up from behind and use the stake on him while he was standing still. Unfortunately, in planning this new technique, we had visualized our officer as being bareheaded, but now we discovered that they all wore caps, so we had to improvise once more and remove some of the cloths to re-establish the balance.

The officer sat down on the pavement. Trembling with excitement, we unbuttoned his leather holster, but it was empty, his pistol was not there. "What's going on?" the officer was muttering. We leaned him against a wall and went away.

Traitors, cowards, I thought. They haven't even got pistols to put in their officers' holsters. Bastards. So we gave up this system of acquiring pistols; in the end we got some from the local *popolani*, who somehow did manage to return home with pistols in their pockets. They are better than we are, I thought. We weren't taught the right things at school.

The whole province was in a ferment. People were getting together, counting their numbers, concealing arms; the families approved, the priests warily gave their blessing. There was a general feeling of rebellion, an impatient and radical desire to say no. People were thoroughly disgusted with the war, and also, though in a confused sort of way, with the system that had wanted it in the first place and had subsequently made such a grotesque mess of it, and ultimately with the whole society of which the regime had been an expression. People wanted to put an end to the entire business, to start again; we were living in a sort of void in the country's history, there was room for something new, something decent and responsible. Of course all this was pretty tentative, and mixed with anger against the destruction-crazy Germans, as well as with a good dose of that age-old Italian obsession: parochialism. The phrase most often heard was "save the town" (which meant, chiefly, the houses in the center, the bridge over the river, and the electric power plant) —save it from the reprisals that were expected from the retreating Germans. For there was still a feeling of their retreat being imminent, of the end being in sight. But one did, deep down, sense the waves of a collective impulse; we were in the middle of a genuine popular movement and it was intoxicating. One was aware of the surging power of things that come from below, and had a feeling of warmth and confidence in being carried by the powerful tide of the general sense of determination.

"How very peculiar," Lelio and I used to say; "there really does seem to be such a thing as the will of the people." We had seen so many slogans about the will of the Italian people scrawled on walls by order of the regime; in Fascist Italy, when you saw a thing written on a wall, it meant that it was definitely false, so we had taken it for granted that there was no such thing as the will of the Italian people. And now here it was for all to see and we were in the very midst of it. We couldn't help thinking of Lenin and his friends and how they must have felt when they arrived at the Finland station, and saw what they saw and began to act: and we regretted our inadequacy.

We traveled from village to village establishing "contacts," assigning responsibilities, drawing up lists, talking to the priest, to the local schoolmaster, to students and ex-servicemen. It was wonderfully enjoyable work; our province is beautiful, and we found that we had really known little about it. But now the Resistance gave us the pretext of going everywhere—by bicycle, of course, an excellent way of seeing places. We went into houses, presbyteries, inns, cowsheds, and shops; we saw how the people lived, how they went about their lives. Our towns and villages were still in disarray because of the war; they had a provisional, uncertain look about them. The people had not really learned yet how to settle down to normal life, and the families still revolved around the womenfolk, as well as the old and the children; the men, only just back, seemed almost to be there on loan.

Everywhere, Lelio and I found the familiar flagged kitchens, the parlors where the roof timbers showed, the courtyards and barns and stables; we drank water from copper buckets; we sat on worn wickerwork chairs, and on stone hearthsides. It was an open conspiracy, sometimes it was indoors and sometimes out on the square, with people from our own district: a conspiracy in dialect, as it were. We were touched by the way they acted and spoke. As we journeyed from place to place, we would talk about poetry, philosophy, and above all about aesthetics; because in the midst of all this havoc, we still believed that aesthetics was supremely important. Nearly all my friends thought so. It seems strange now, but so it was.

Little by little we had grown into an organization; now there were *comitati*, committees, and we were already using the word "clandestine"; formal meetings were held, lists of persons compiled under various headings—place of birth, Christian name, surname, nickname, home address, number of pistols, rifles, amounts of ammunition held—everything in fact that the Fascist police would want to know, to get a really clear, detailed picture. The political and military sections began to be separated into distinct bodies, and people specialized according to their particular bents; many had chosen false names for themselves, though it was easier to call them by their real ones. Some were manifestly reliable people, others manifestly not; the most impressive seemed to us the *fuoriusciti*, the silent, shriveled political exiles who had now turned up from no one really knew where. One of these, a Communist, we found in a village in the Prealpi, and there we used to visit him. He was a gruff-voiced elderly little man, who had fought in Spain; he exuded glory and sadness, the sadness of the long road that had led to this mountain village where he was now biding his time. In the afternoons, by way of relaxation, he used to ride on horse-back along the paths behind the village, and people would whisper: "There goes the General." He was a sad general. He used to talk to us about the ethics of Communism; he said that one should concentrate on being more honest, loyal, and unselfish than one's fellows, and then, he said, the rest would follow as a matter of course. We used to listen to him; we were both thrilled and awestruck. We belonged to the Action Party, the newest and most advanced of the clandestine parties. We thought we were the keepers of the Communist Party's conscience—and perhaps of everybody else's as well. We admired the Communists profoundly. Actually some of the Communists we had to deal with, especially the very young ones, were rather exasperating; they were extremely good at practical things, but one could never have the pleasure of a real, rational argument with them; they always seemed to choose not to understand the points we made, points which seemed to us so subtle, fair-minded, and human. It was as if they were driving in a nail, with a few deft strokes of the hammer; when it was our turn to talk they did stop and listen, but every now and then they would give another tap with the hammer, still on the same nail, as if we had not been there at all. All the same they commanded great respect; they were obviously up to their necks in the New Italy, they were always the first in every-thing, always in the van, never calculating and always ready to accept the consequences. It is no good saying now that they *must* have been calculating; people who say this have understood nothing of the Communists of the time; but we saw them with our own eyes and we know how genuine and admirable they were. One could not help contrasting them with those school friends of ours, from Vicenza and Padua, who kept going with their Kierkegaard or Jaspers— perhaps while in hiding at an aunt's in the country—or even went on working at their university examinations, so as not to fall behind in their careers (and in between whiles maybe

38

turning out the odd hermetic lyric or two). There were plenty of people like these, and today many of them are advanced progressives; let's hope they succeeded in making good careers for themselves and also that they feel a pang of shame before going to sleep.

The arrests had started too. The Fascists had now set up a special "political" police at Vicenza, and already it was clear there was going to be a race for time between ourselves and them; but with every week that passed, and with the war at a standstill at the other end of Italy, the chances of our taking over before they did became fainter. We tried now to act with a certain amount of circumspection, to cut out unnecessary meetings. I had a small notebook on the cover of which I had written *CAHIER JAUNE* and which I used to fill with figures and initials, tearing out the pages once I had finished with them. Indeed, one realizes now only too well that it was we who virtually compelled the other side to resort to torture. I found that book recently in the attic; three or four pages had writing on them: an abstract geometry of syllables, laid out in neat patterns, splendid stuff; I no longer understand a word of it.

The autumn was coming to an end. My grandfather died; I was there at the time, in the bare room, and witnessed this solemn event. Winter came. Things stiffened around us, began to firm up. At the start there had been hardly any distinction between active members of the organization and just sympathizers. Some of the latter did a good job, and others tried hard; but there were also some who got mixed up about the issues. One of them did carry a suitcase of ammunition, but he also carried some gold in it—whether stolen or just smuggled, I don't know; he was definitely doing it on a private basis and not for the greater glory of God. Another got off a bus one day, delivered his message, then pulled out a small pistol and shot himself right in the chest, I don't remember whether it was for love or because of debts, but once again it was for personal reasons. Yet another had stored at his home in Vicenza a rucksack full of explosives, about half a hundredweight, but on hearing the front doorbell ring, one day, he lost his nerve, tipped the explosives down the toilet, and pulled the chain. For days we feared for the safety of the citizens of Vicenza, unaware of what was circulating in their sewers.

One by one such auxiliaries were now going out of circulation: one disappeared with his brother's fiancée, one got arrested in a brawl, others simply went off to see distant relatives and when we called at their houses to fetch whatever it was they'd failed to deliver, their mothers would say to us: "He's gone to Sardinia, and left this package"; and this package would be a sort of farewell to arms and to us.

And so in the end we were left to ourselves, to the original handful of friends. People were being arrested daily: it was clear that it would soon be our turn. Reports began to circulate about the special treatment reserved for political prisoners, and it was noticeable that one arrest tended to produce others, which in turn brought about still more, as in a chain reaction. One day in February—my birthday—I heard that a satellite of ours, who had a special allergy to torture, had been arrested. I took the precaution of going to what had been my grandparents' house farther down the *paese*, and stayed shut up there all day. Sure enough, two or three men in civilian clothes called at my home; they ill-treated my family a little, but not much, and they didn't take anybody away. They were still inexperienced. The day passed sadly at my grandparents' house; the old people were both dead now, and most uncles and aunts were away; the place was empty and dark. At midday I found myself alone at the table with my aunt Nina, and as I ate I told her that it was my birthday.

"How old are you?" she asked; I said I was twenty-two. My aunt began to cry. "You poor boy," she said. "You're old, and you've not even known what it is to be young." I went upstairs to read Russo's *Elogio della Polemica*; I felt that my aunt was right, I was old. All the same, I felt that I still had not fired the last rounds of my youth. *Gesù Bambino,* please let me fire them one day, I thought to myself.

Something like this happened to all my companions. We had done what we could, disregarding studies and private interests, though occasionally someone was permitted to ease off, if it were for some particular reason or other, such as the arrest of a brother. In a case like this it was generally agreed that the other brother should be allowed to do some of his exams. And so, during that bleak winter, there were a few of us who still carried on with their studies; working in those icy rooms, they would put two mattresses on the floor, then lie in between, with a balaclava on the head. This only went on by day, however. In the evenings balaclavas would be removed, and out these boys would go, like the rest of us, with a pail of whitewash to daub slogans on walls, or with sabotage equipment. The sabotage we did was pretty modest, virtually invisible; our slogans were huge. Literary inclinations always came to the fore; the texts of our slogans were ingenious, almost too much so.

This was the moment when the idea of going up into the mountains came to us. We felt utterly at a loss and alone: there were no public institutions any more in Italy; nothing that one could turn to. There did remain, of course (besides the new sinister organizations of the Neofascist Party—which were to us alien bodies, a disease), certain private possibilities, the families skulking in their houses, the women at work, the priests in their churches, and then of course the poets, the books; anyone who wanted could withdraw himself into some private cocoon and stay there waiting. But this was not for us, and it never occurred to us to do it.

The only thing that still seemed important to us in the midst of all the shambles was the bond we felt with the cultural and intellectual opposition. We were only beginners, neophytes; yet we came to feel that we ourselves were now responsible for this tradition, and as it could not be protected on the spot, it was up to us to take these mysteries and carry them away. The cities were contaminated, the plains swarming with German columns, and in the villages the black-shirted crowd reappeared, the functionaries of chaos. We had to go up into the mountains.

It may well be asked, looking back, why—following this initial impulse—there failed to be a great popular uprising, a really overwhelming one. Why didn't we deliberately try to bring it about? The truth was that we hadn't really *understood* the implications of the situation.

When I reread Mazzini on the "war of armed bands," it makes me gnaw my fingers. There it all is already. He knew the answers a hundred years in advance.

We must resort to a different method of war, a method which must come from the nation itself, out of its very essence. . . .

A war of armed bands: *this is the kind of war that will provide anyone, capable and confident enough, with the opportunity for fame and action, for it makes each man king and master in his own field, by kindling emulation and fostering initiative. . . . Even hatred and revenge, in themselves disgraceful things, turn into sacred and noble passions when the victims are foreign oppressors.*

This, then, should have been our aim: we should have proclaimed a popular war, we should have revealed to the people the extent of their own powers, we should have taught them a way to wage war that did not demand specialized skills, training, or materials, but only courage and vigor, familiarity with the countryside, imagination and cunning. We should have pointed to the Austrians, and told the people: Their gold, their weapons, their horses are yours if you care to get them.

And all this could have been done: it would have been

enough for a few veterans to show the way, and make them-
selves leaders of the young; flags should have been hoisted
in the villages, in the fields, on the church towers; firearms
handed out or, failing that, the people could have made
themselves spears and daggers. . . .

. . . Yes, and files too.

So that was the answer. Insurrection had to be proclaimed *immediately*. Not just resistance, but insurrection; a political and popular war had to be set in motion at once. Let's go down to the villages, this evening, now. Let's call the people into the piazza, beat the drums, hoist the flags, put out the portraits—the King, the Pope, Lenin all together: all the world is with us. Long live the Soviets! Long live Jesus and the Eucharist!

It would have been simple to have got a revolution going; the Alto Vicentino would have burst into flames in a matter of hours. That's what we ought to have done; but we didn't. And so, if there is a committee in the next world that assesses and judges patriotic merit, it will never forgive us.

Naturally, they would soon have exterminated us, prob-ably in the first flare-up, certainly in the second or third. But at least Italy would have had a taste of what it really means to be renewed through and through; and our grave-stones today would be revered by a nation that was alto-gether better.

We missed the opportunity, we didn't know the right texts. Those of our friends who probably did know them, like Antonio and young Franco, were away, up in the Alps, or in jail; and it occurs to me that they may well have re-frained deliberately from sending us even a short biblio-graphical list of references on a postcard, because they knew our temperaments too well and feared that we might overdo it. At any rate we had got nowhere during the autumn; then it was winter, and we had reached these straits; and so by the end of the winter we had found ourselves at a loss and alone.

We thought: There is nothing left to defend except a tiny nugget of anti-Fascism—honor, if you like; Italy has gone to pot; let's get away, let us go up into the mountains. It was a retreat from the world, a flight into the Thebaid.

I have said that we were at a loss and alone: that is a manner of speaking.

Marta had a country house, on a rise between two little valleys in the hills; she had quantities of wonderful books, and kept a kind of court, or refuge, where every manner of person went. She had decided to protect us too; it was all done privately, but her house was an important center and as chaotic as a public council. She immediately invented a new identity for me and produced a set of papers, a simple matter for her; she made me much younger than I really was so that I would not be eligible for call-up. She warned me not to start a conversation unnecessarily. "When you open your mouth, you seem grown up," she said.

I used to get up at sunrise. With my mouth firmly shut, I worked all morning on the land with the peasants; we were digging a huge trench for planting vines. In the afternoon I had a bath and then read books. It made me think that being kept could be very pleasant.

Marta did a lot for us; but she was always so busy that any extra piece of work she took on was lost and consumed in the conflagration of her energy like a twig thrown into a bonfire. She came and went from the town continuously, partly because she had a job there—indeed, I suspect she had two jobs.

She really was an unusual woman; she had been every-where, she knew everybody. The Tirol, Edinburgh, Milan, Tripoli, she was familiar with them all. Scholars have cal-culated that, in his long, industrious life, Croce can have spent only about half an hour studying Plato: considering

44

what else he had read, he can't possibly have had time for more. Similarly, she could have devoted only about half an hour to the Dordogne and five minutes to Pantelleria, but she had a rich *rapport* with them both. She was nurse, instructress, farmer, interpreter; and she was always ready to do anything for anybody or any family. She had an adventurous, romantic way of helping people: she would appear suddenly, often in disguise (but then she always seemed to be slightly in disguise), she loved to barge right into somebody's life, into a family, and turn it inside out. She often picked on casual acquaintances or traveling companions, or relatives of subtenants of relatives. She would bring them presents, offers of employment, travel tickets, recipes for Scottish dishes; then she would seize some member of the family and bear him off on a journey—probably slightly in disguise as well, say in an Irish scarf or a Brazilian cap of the very best quality.

September 8th must have caught her fancy, for she immediately adopted the Vicenza Resistance *en bloc,* not in the sense that she had dealings with all its members, but in the sense that every representative, every aspect she came across was automatically her own. She believed all of us to be splendid people, each one more splendid than the last, worthy to have any amount of care lavished on him. The most remarkable thing about her was that she was not at all bossy (except in little things, like forcing cold risotto on me in the mornings, meant to be in imitation of Scotch porridge, and thus indicative of worldliness); indeed, she was always stressing the unimportance of her functions—their menial nature.

Actually her functions were not menial at all. There was nothing of the conventional nurse-image—self-denying, spreading balm. What she did was creative and inventive. She was an inventor; she invented just as others laugh or cry; with her we all felt in a world of fantasy, totally unpredictable. Half Florence Nightingale, half Mata Hari, she adored mystifying people, especially when it was not strictly necessary. Having got us equipped with false identity cards, bronze knuckle-dusters and the like (she had a blind faith in bronze weapons), she would also want to dress us up, preferably as women. She would seize on any excuse to attempt to make us dress as women. But as we rather objected to this, she had to fall back on disguising herself. She would have preferred to dress really impressively, as a sergeant in the *carabinieri*, or an Austrian officer of the First War; but then she would settle for triter models: a beggar with a stick, an old peasant with a colored kerchief around her head and a basket of violets, or a fortuneteller. Strangely enough, the more she disguised herself, the more recognizable she became. When she went up to friends with a pannier on her back and her face smeared with grime, they would say: "Darling, how wonderful. You're looking so well today."

Just before we left for the mountains, mainly to keep her happy we tried to dress Bene as a woman, with high heels and a veil; he was exactly like a tart and this would have been all right. But it is incredible how large a man dressed as a woman can seem: especially Bene, who was rather well built in any case. He looked like an immense whore, a Cyclopean cow, and—as a matter of fact—very beautiful. He was so large that obviously he would have been arrested for public indecency simply on account of his dimensions; so we undressed him and I remember that even in his vest and pants he seemed very, very big.

I felt I too must have a try. So I put on lipstick, a black, short, close-fitting dress and high heels, and stuck two potatoes in my bosom; then I put on earrings and a hat with a veil, and went to have a look at myself in the mirror. The laugh died on my lips. I was lovely.

Quickly I undressed myself.

Marta got hold of all sorts of elegant grips and valises for us—Orient Express sort of stuff; inside these we put our haversacks, woolen pullovers, and sundry weapons, ancient and modern. Then we boarded a train with her and she assigned us our various parts: one of us was to be her cousin, another an idiot, another just an acquaintance. She found the idea of escorting us as far as the mountains amusing. As yet there were no partisan units near Vicenza, so we proposed to establish one in the Bellunese, where we knew that Antonio had now moved. We arrived at a little station just short of Belluno—Nello, Bene, and I—and this was where we had our nocturnal rendezvous with Antonio.

For a brief moment, as we shook hands, I saw satisfaction on his face, almost a kind of relief that I too had come. I was pleased at his pleasure, but also a little disturbed. It had not occurred to me that he was not already certain that I would be there. Perhaps Antonio underestimated the extent of his own influence; and of course he was so used to finding himself isolated—and to seeing people (and history) going wrong. Momentarily, therefore, I was a little sad at not having had his complete and unquestioning confidence, which I felt I deserved.

The haversacks were taken out of the smart valises, and we put them on our backs. Then we started walking toward the mountains.

4

IN THE BELLUNESE there is a valley, long, narrow, and twisted like a bowel, known as the Canal del Mis. It took us a long time to get there. No doubt our guides knew what they were doing; I didn't. We seemed to be making no progress; at one moment we were walking toward the tall mountains, at another away from them, in pitch dark. There were hamlets, fields, banks, shingly river beds, dark village streets, silent houses. We crept around whispering.

It was a relief when at long last those who guided us made straight for the mountain range, and soon I realized we were entering the Canal del Mis. We passed between what looked like great sluices and buttressed recesses, and all at once I perceived the structure of the long, bare furrow in front of us. We walked for a while along the empty road at the bottom of the valley; suddenly a path on the right hooked itself to the groin of the mountain; we took it, and began to climb steeply until we were high in the black air.

48

We walked for hours in total darkness, then stopped in the middle of nowhere. We had arrived.

Gropingly we explored the little clearing; the shepherd's hut was bolted. The place was called Landrina; it was snowing. The men who had come with us went down again. We were left alone on the dark shoulder of the night, Nello, Bene, and I.

There was a pigsty next to the hut, and we went in there to sleep. At last, I thought, now we are partisans.

Bene, curled up in the straw between Nello and me, grumbled and panted. The pigsty in some ways was shut in, in others it wasn't; it appeared to be leaning against a dry wall, and was made of planks. Brisk little drafts came through the gaps between the planks, and Bene kept waking up and complaining about them; he was very sensitive to drafts, he said that later we would pay for them, after we were thirty or forty. I was a bit surprised that he was interested in those absurd, distant ages.

"Keep still," I said, because he kept turning over. We had one blanket between us, and as he was in the middle he uncovered Nello and me alternately.

Some specks of snow also came through the gaps; every now and then I felt one settling on my face, and in a second it would melt. It was like being in a fairy story. We were absurdly alone, for miles and miles and miles.

"God, what a night," said Bene.

"Go to sleep," I said; but I knew that he was happy, though a little baffled, as I was: I could tell it from the way he was grumbling. Nello said nothing. He was to be the first of my friends to die; and all my memories of him during those months seem to be individually significant. I felt the snowflakes settling on my eyelids, and their brief struggle before expiring.

In the morning we found that the place was quite attractive, rather bare but not wild: we were on a kind of terrace

49

facing south. Immediately I found myself looking at the entrances to the paths and calculating how we could organize cross fires in case somebody unpleasant decided to attack us.

The idea at the moment was purely hypothetical; the only real fire we could have was a wood one, assuming we managed to light it, and our first attempts were not at all promising.

I looked at these entrances trying mentally to enfilade them with nonexistent machine guns. I saw very well that the idea in practice was hopeless. All right, but what else could we do? I tried to talk it over with Bene, but all he said was: "You went through an officer cadets' training course, didn't you? It's your problem."

Well, I thought, how *are* we supposed to fight this war? When we were on the course we learned principally about storming trenches. What about sending a special message to the Germans, if they started to climb up here, asking them to dig trenches for us to storm? But they weren't sporting enough for this, and—come to think of it—I had only learned how to storm trenches on the flat—not in mountain country.

The sun was high; we were watching the path down to the valley when suddenly we heard voices to our rear. Our clearing had already been invaded, people had arrived from the opposite side. We've made a fine start, I thought. Luckily, the new arrivals were friendly, our first recruits in fact.

Several others arrived that day and on the next. At one point I saw someone far away down the path climbing in a wooden, angry manner, kicking at stones. He was fair-haired and sulky-looking: it was Lelio. We had been expecting him, but up in the mountains it was always a great pleasure to see friends actually arrive; subsequently I saw many more come, in various places and circumstances, and each time I felt moved.

In two or three days our little detachment was complete. Besides the four of us from Vicenza—the nucleus, we considered ourselves—there were fifteen to twenty local *popolani*, some too young to have been in the Army, but mostly veterans from the Russian and Balkan fronts. One of these men was a cook and immediately set to work; he was excellent. To come all the way up there just to be a cook seemed a bit of a shame, but he was not much interested in anything else. We usually ate once a day, but well and in abundance. H.Q. down in the plain must have been sweating with the effort to keep us supplied.

Mixed up with these *popolani* there were also three or four boys from the plain. One was from Venice itself and of course knew little about dry land, let alone the mountains; we called him Ballotta, and he had ulcers. I don't remember where he had these ulcers, but he certainly did have them somewhere; his efforts to be a partisan, with them inside him, and he being so far from the lagoons, were rather touching. He did not know how to march or carry things, or fire weapons (which didn't matter much for the time being), or find his bearings. Basically he could do no more than carry on a continuous struggle against his ulcers; but he attached great importance to being able to do so up there. After a few weeks we had forcibly to deliver him to some relatives he had in the Agordino, and there we left him. He started to cry, and it occurred to me that if medals meant anything, the first really big one ought to be given to him.

Technically speaking, the boys from the plain, all students more or less, were rather poor military material. They didn't understand the mountains, still less the notion of a partisan band—however embryonic. They would disappear behind bushes, where we would find them sitting, pale and ashamed, with their trousers unbuttoned. I thought I might proclaim the freedom of masturbation, just to give those poor fellows a charter; but I was advised against this.

There were also two university students from Padua, brothers and both fine fellows. One had a guitar, and he immediately began to compose a song, both words and music, for our detachment; the other spoke to me about the Jesuits, how they were so very brilliant in manipulating ideas and people.

I hated that song from the start. It ran: *The night is dark, the wind is cold, the partisan is very bold.* This could just about pass, but then there were other lines which went: *He thinks of Mother, and sweetheart dear, the only girl for whom he can care;* and this was too much. However, the Bellunesi considered that the song was full of subtle meaning. Sometimes I was driven to think that anything said, or even sung, in Italian as distinct from dialect, becomes corrupt.

Nor did I find the Jesuits convincing, either. Oh, shut up, I used to think, let's talk about war, for God's sake. But when we talked about war the two boys from Padua kept on saying: "Wait, wait . . . we've got to wait and see." I realized that these two represented common sense, but I lost my patience. "This is a time of crisis," I wanted to say to them, "what's the use of common sense?"

I was in command. Actually, I didn't want to be in command, and tried to refuse, but they told me not to fuss, so I did my best. We occupied the shepherd's hut, which gave a good deal more shelter than the pigsty. Toward evening we lit the fire, and soon we got accustomed to the smoke, which was light, pungent, and aromatic. Weapons were scarce: two rifles, two or three pistols, a few bayonets, a small bag of bullets, not all suitable for the rifles or pistols. "We can always throw them," said Bene.

In the evening, in this hut, the Bellunesi boys, having finished the detachment's lugubrious theme song, sang their own songs in the smoke. I had only known the expurgated versions, but the full ones were wonderful.

"What a song," I would whisper to Bene.

"Very spontaneous," he answered, because when I wanted

to praise something I used to say it was spontaneous, and he was always laughing at me about this.

Some of the Bellunesi were deferential, some were prudently cordial, others kept quiet. We must inspire them with confidence, I said to myself. The relations between us and them seemed to me all wrong, as if we could never really get on the same footing.

I had read in various semiclandestine books about the virtues of self-government, so I thought: We must have self-government. Immediately I appointed a strongly autonomous vice-commandant; he had been a sergeant in Russia and was a good man, serious and rather reserved, aged about twenty-eight.

"What was it like in Russia?" I asked him.

"A Russian girl was in love with me."

He was not much concerned with the military aspect. "I spent most of my time with this Russian," he said. "She had three children too."

"What language did you speak?"

"Oh, *nema kukurush*, that sort of thing."

He was an introvert. There was another sergeant who was an extrovert; he made us carry haversacks full of beans, to keep fit. When I gave a wrong order he would say: "Excuse me, *Comandante*, but I think that order's wrong. I will of course do what you ask, though," so I would change the order.

I was determined that there should be self-government, but having told the others not to use the area near the hut as a latrine, and then having found much evidence of disobedience among the bushes, I called an Excrement Meeting. We held it just where I had found the Excrement. I stood in the center and vigorously harangued the detachment, pointing at the Excrement with my finger. I spoke about discipline, self-discipline, the Italian ruling classes, Italy in general, and humanity. Bene had never been in the

Army and liked this performance very much, but in fact I do not think that it was a good idea. What I was doing was not even original: there had been Excrement Meetings on the cadet course, run by my Captain, the one with the glass eye. In fact, I was simply copying him.

Some of the faces of my companions gathered around me looked distinctly disconcerted. They were people who had been in the war while we were at Padua arguing over Quasimodo. I felt that I had been re-creating a barracks atmosphere, and I was overcome with shame. This is not being a partisan, I said to myself: this is *la naia*, military service, all over again, indeed an inferior imitation of it. However, the technical problem still remained. What a rotten education we've had, I thought: we know about the Homeric question, the laws of thermodynamics, and the themes of Provençal lyrics; but we simply can't cope with excrements.

Although I was in command, I naturally took my turn at guard duty like all the rest. I even chose the worst times, between two and six in the morning, to set a good example. This guard duty was done some hundred yards from the hut; one stood there among the branches, in the middle of the snow, in the dark. In those hours of absolute, icy solitude, one felt one was all sorts of things: a soldier, a monk, a nerve of the universe, and a bit of an idiot. The cold was terrible. During my turn nobody came.

The rations were hauled up from below on a pulley. At the foot of the mountain there was a peasant's house and the pulley started from there; one evening two or three of us went down on a visit, just to make sure that the world still existed, and that the war had not finished during our absence. The family was gathered in the cowshed with the animals; one entered this cowshed by passing through the kitchen. The warmth was marvelous, the stench was hot, from fermentation; our eyes felt as though they were being pricked by needles. There were three cows and a few goats. One of the women was healthy-looking and still young; she seemed fairly appetizing to me, especially in there. I slept that night in the cowshed; my eyes stung even in the darkness. If the war comes to an end, I kept thinking, at least these people are sure to hear.

We all had rather long hair; Bandiera said he knew how to cut hair and I, to set the example, had mine done by him. We had a stool, which we placed in the middle of the clearing. Bandiera had been on leave and had come back with a bag of instruments; he had a pair of ancient scissors and some dented clippers. I sat on the stool. Bandiera tied a rag around my neck and straight away began to butcher me, without any preliminaries. Gradualness didn't come into it. Great globules of tears poured down from my eyes and I swallowed them punctiliously; the whole detachment had gathered around. The sky was overcast and the light on our terrace among the mountains had taken on a dismal, almost funereal color. Bandiera butchered me quickly. I remembered that his real trade was in fact a butcher's; but by now it was too late. When all was over he took out a metal mirror from his bag and gave it to me. I put it a little to one side so that I could look at the most important part of what he had done. At first I couldn't make out anything at all: the surface of the mirror only reflected a strange, whitish, unhealthy-looking patch. Then I noticed that out of the middle of this patch there sprouted an ear, and with a shock I recognized the side of my head. My hair had been extirpated to my temples; underneath there were these whitish patches with green tinges, like something infected with the plague. Above was a tuft of mutilated hairs; I looked like a monk whose ringworm had been treated with verdigris. Bandiera escaped while I hunted for the scissors. When he returned to camp the following day I had got over it. All the same I did want to find out the extent of his experience as a barber, and he confessed that he had only *slept* with a barber, chastely that is; it was one night after September 8th, at Portogruaro, where they had met by chance after being disbanded; and before going to sleep they had talked at some length.

I don't now remember those Bellunesi boys very well; I remember a face, a name, rarely both together, or a voice, and the things they said. I do know that many of them finished up badly, but I have never wanted to find out which ones, or how. In my heart I know very well that they were strung up on the meathooks that the Germans used in that zone; and that horses dragged them away, perhaps before they were dead. How did they behave when this happened? How would we students have behaved, I, in particular, in such circumstances? But a thing like that—how one would have behaved—is not all that significant, although at the time it seemed so important to us.

One day we saw a long line of soldiers marching across a slope toward the camp at Landrina. There was a moment of consternation among us, as when you are driving at night and suddenly see a bridge or tunnel which you know does not exist and you think: I bet this is how accidents happen; but then we observed that they didn't carry weapons either. They were preceded by a small boy of nine or ten; we waited for them in open order, hands in pockets. When they had arrived, the small boy said, in dialect: "We are English." We began to laugh, and the soldiers began to laugh too, when they saw us laughing; then we fraternized. They were from the Eighth Army, ex-prisoners who had escaped at the armistice; they had been living in peasants' houses in the area, and spoke of their hosts with frank admiration.

Having established that they wanted to be enrolled with us, I assembled them in a circle and said, in English:

"Do you want to be soldiers or cooks?"

I said this as clearly as I could, and with great seriousness, proud to show how democratic we were and how we respected the wishes of individual recruits. Perhaps, if there had been a member of the ruling classes among them, he would have replied with one of those dry and elliptical jokes which I suppose they are taught at school. Instead, being working-class, they did not mind explaining a bit; indeed, they became quite didactic, and from what they said I concluded that the Eighth Army must be an association of cook-soldiers, or soldier-cooks; so we enrolled them in both capacities, but of course after the first trial we kept them away from the kitchen.

They were regular soldiers, the first that I really came to know; it is true that I had some cousins who were regular sergeants and warrant officers in various branches of the Italian Forces, but (apart from the fact that a noncommissioned officer is not really a soldier) the general attitude was different. With my cousins the be-all and end-all of everything was one's uniform, number of stripes, pay, the day's schedule. With these English soldiers everything centered around physical stamina. They were people of normal aspect, but they were "tough," an intriguing English word which means that you can be pushed to the limit of endurance. If they had to carry loads, they would carry them, if they had to march, they would march. Sometimes they would take off their boots and expose some really spectacular blisters on which they had been marching for hours without saying anything, except their one little, favorite swear-word. Some of our men, being from the mountains, were stronger than they were, and quicker at marching in the mountains, but they were not so "tough" in enduring, without protest, hunger and thirst and blisters and all the rest.

Soon we began to understand one another pretty well; they were curious about the basic words in our language such as *cramento* and *mona*, we about their most important expression, which seemed to us to be a compendium of what the average Englishman thinks and feels about nature and society: it sounded like *fochinau*. They liked our song about the girl Rosina, visited by five *alpini*, all at the same time, one fine evening; we liked theirs about seven green bottles, and one or two others. They could not really grasp the concept of blasphemy; we explained patiently that this is an important Catholic institution, and tried to show them how it works. They pretended to understand, but they didn't. A real blasphemy—with a subject and a predicate—is in fact incomprehensible to those who haven't the true faith. However, they did understand the song about the chimney-sweep, and applied it to all the leading American film stars, whom they pictured having their pudenda blackened in turn.

They did not take part in any of our discussions or decisions; they stood around, looking rather than listening; now that they had joined our group, they were ready to follow us loyally and incuriously. We could not tell whether they considered themselves obliged to stay with us for some patriotic reason, or through some code of professional honor of their own, or from an obscure private preference. Some were obviously undermined in morale by years of prison, they seemed taciturn and emptied; one realized this by the absent, vaguely mad way of staring at you that they had. One of them might suddenly disappear, without saying anything, during the night, and in the morning when we were looking for him his companions would say: "Perhaps he is trying to get to Switzerland."

The others, with some reticence, allowed themselves to become our friends. One felt that they must have an inner life of their own, some private feelings and emotions which, because of the language and through their reserve, remained hidden from us. Walter kept a diary, and we wondered what outpourings and reflections went into it. Bene made him show us a page; under the date only two words were written:

"Weather glorious."

The adjective pleased us enormously. At least something was glorious.

We said to each other that we would get going as soon as we had a few weapons. Meanwhile, however, we made preparations. We tried to train the nonmountaineers; we made them spend hours under haversacks filled with beans (H.Q. was indefatigable in supplying us with beans), although there were moments when it seemed to me that these exercises served to exhaust them more than anything else.

The few weapons we had were almost a disadvantage. One had to polish them, count them, guard them; we even had to make an arms-rack to keep them in good order. And anyhow they were so few and so old.

"Are those weapons any use, if someone attacks?" a student from the plain timidly asked.

"No," said the extrovert sergeant.

"No," I promptly repeated.

"Then why don't we bury them somewhere?" asked the student from the plain. "It would be less dangerous."

On this point I was certainly not prepared to compromise, but I didn't have to make a speech about it. The entire detachment, whether they were from Vicenza, Padua, or Belluno, were ready to say no too. The weapons were our status symbol. I cordially hated them because they were so few and ugly and old; but they were sacred.

We've got to wake up, I thought: go down to the plain by night, take risks, get to know the area. In war, as in life, one must seize the initiative.

I gathered everybody together and made a little oration: "*Compagni*," I said, secretly quoting.* "Do we want to stay here eating polenta? Do we want to wait for the enemy to mop us up? We must take the initiative. We must go into action. Whatever actions we do may be small, but they must be continuous, one after the other. We'll learn as we go along, maybe we'll have to forget as we go along too."

"What sort of actions?" asked one of the Padovani.

"Ambushes?" I asked dramatically, to cover up my uncertainty. "Arrests? Sabotage? Roundups? Anything will do."

* Dante, but inaccurately.

"But where? How?" asked the Padovano.

"Up to you," I said.

"Let's have a go at blowing up something," said the extrovert sergeant. We had a few explosives, but we had already used up half of them on training—and they had cost two or three trees behind the hut their lives. These explosions up in the mountains had been pretty hefty, so that the people down in the valley had said: "Hear that? They've got artillery."

The idea of blowing up something appealed to everybody, even the Padovani. There just remained the problem of choosing the place where we were to have this go. The bridge at the entrance of the canal was conveniently sited, but once we'd sent it up, with its balls in the air, as we say in our dialect, we would have caused more inconvenience to ourselves than to the enemy. The railway line, in the plain, was a genuine military objective; but Bene, who had a highly developed civic conscience, thought of the first train that would come along, and said: "What about the engineer? And the fireman?"

Finally we chose the power station. There were civic and human problems, even here, but when you get down to it there are problems everywhere. Plans were ready, jobs assigned, a haversack filled with explosives. There just remained authorization from H.Q.; a mere formality, but I felt that this would put things in the clear. But H.Q. sent up a dispatch rider with this message: "Are you mad? Don't you dare touch the power station."

"Shall we just murder someone?" said the extrovert sergeant.

"A *crucco*?" * suggested Lelio. "Three of us could go down in patrol and the first German we come across will be in for it."

"A collaborator might be better."

"But what if he's doing a double bluff?"

* Slang for a German, e.g., Kraut, Boche.

60

"We could ask H.Q."

"Are you mad?" the word came from H.Q. "Don't you dare murder anybody."

"H.Q. doesn't want us to murder anybody."

"Oh, somebody go and shit in their mouths."

So three of us went down to the plain, not necessarily to carry out this threat, but in search of inspiration.

It was still cold, and over our civilian clothes we wore military overcoats. In the right-hand pocket of my overcoat (which was gigantic) I had a little revolver, a sort of woman's toy, a boudoir thing. The province was one of those that had been taken over directly by the Germans, and paradoxically this made it much safer at night, because Italian police and *carabinieri* were not very keen to help the Germans, and so in effect we did not run any real risk. I felt a little like Pinocchio, when he wandered about at night; there were dangers, but artificial ones. Everything was a little artificial.

Out of the darkness there came a challenge from the *carabinieri*: "*Alto-là.*" We were practically on top of them. We were standing in the harsh beam of a torch. Nello was in the middle, holding a bicycle. "Hands up," the *carabinieri* said. Up went our hands, and the bicycle fell on the ground; from the beam of light there emerged the barrels of two rifles. A *carabiniere* started to search us. Bene and Nello hadn't anything; on me he found the pistol. As he was taking it, I shouted: "Look out, for God's sake!" because I didn't know what else to say. He jumped and withdrew his hand. Then I gave him the pistol and said: "Didn't you realize it was loaded?" Now I began to plead. "*Signor giandarme,*" * I said to the older of the *carabinieri*, "you can see we don't look like thieves and scoundrels." I told him that we meant no harm to anybody, that perhaps he had sons at home . . . perhaps their mother . . . He was distinctly disturbed, and I felt a bit of a fraud. At any rate he took us to

* The word used for policeman in *Pinocchio*.

61

the barracks; but he did it very politely and when we were there he decided to let us go. Naturally we promised that in future we would be good. To get the pistol back, next day, I had to send a friend in H.Q. to fetch it; he was also a friend of the head *giandarme*. So the pistol was sent back to me; it was so tiny it wouldn't have done harm to any vertebrate. This is not war, I thought; this is *Pinocchio*.

It seemed to us that everything devolved on this problem of action. We had observed the poverty and the penury in which the population of the valley lived, so eight or ten of us went in a truck to steal cheese from a big dairy, in order to distribute it among the people.

Four of us were hoisted through a window; we somersaulted into the darkness, fragrant with milk. I was the second to go in, and with my burglar's flashlight I saw that the first man was practically upside down in a vat of thick cream, which he was eating. The shutters were closed: I turned on the light. One of the other two was a *popolano*, he too at once plunged into the vat; the other was a chemistry student, and he didn't plunge. The place was spacious, clean, and tidy. After a little we induced our companions to pull themselves the right way up and we explored the milky kingdom. There was a pretty floor made of red tiles; there were big, scrubbed wooden tables, vats, pots, pans; it was a wonderful land of milk; we had surprised it in its sleep. Even the kingdom of milk suffers violence, I said to myself. A door opened onto the immense province of cheese. All these cheeses slept like good Christians in beds layered one above the other. The corridors were narrow and dark, the cheeses crowded together as though in a huge dormitory, in the catacombs. It occurred to me that if the first Christians had these cheeses in their catacombs, perhaps they would never have felt the need to emerge into the light of the sun, and we up here would still be pagans and all our blasphemies would be about bloody Mars and that whore Minerva, while down below they would certainly have become more and more saintly, and would gradually have lost their sight.

We went and opened up to the others, who meanwhile had driven the truck up to the front door. There followed a saturnalia of cheese and cream eating. At first I thought it would be all right to allow it to go on, then I vainly tried to restrain it; in the end it died down and developed into a mere transportation of cheeses. There was a sense of waste about the whole thing, both of energy and of cheese. We staggered about in circles, rather wildly, as we carried out our loads.

I felt myself almost drowned in a huge Sargasso Sea; it seemed to me that the great cheeses being carried off by force—tossing and swaying above our heads—were like the remains of a shipwreck in a rough sea. I repeated to myself: This is action, action.

The action continued for about half an hour.

In the end we had loaded some twenty hundredweight of lovely round, solid, fragrant cheeses; and so we went away into the night. I was in the rear, among the cheeses. I looked out and saw roads, bends, hedges, crossroads, villages, dark shapes of houses, all slipping away backwards; I didn't recognize anything. It was all a strange charade; I kept on thinking of the *Risorgimento*, and of Bakunin too. Nobody stopped us, which—although we had all our weapons with us—was a very good thing.

We had sent proper receipts in closed envelopes for this requisition, with a series of vouchers, invented by ourselves and honorably signed. But the fellows at the provincial H.Q., when they heard about what we had done, expressed indignation instead of pleasure, and decided to pay for the cheeses we had captured. It was now our turn to be indignant, but in the end we said: *Fate vobis.*

Our intention, as I have said, was not to keep the cheeses for ourselves, we only meant to taste and then distribute them among the people. This part of the plan we managed to put into practice. We went around presenting cheeses to the people of the Agordino, in the name of the Italian people. The people of the Agordino appreciated the gesture, I don't know about the Italian people; however, the people of the Agordino were also a bit upset, not because of the origin of the cheeses but because of the possible consequences. They didn't say no to our gifts, but they didn't pluck up enough courage to eat them. We wanted them to start immediately but they stood about craven-hearted and reluctant. So we had to cut some of the cheeses ourselves, a little theatrically, with our bayonets, and offer the pieces around, though not always with much success. Undernourishment is a strange affair. We almost lost our temper with the most obstinate of them: "Go on, eat up, damn you!" we cried; bayonets in hand, disheveled, and rather fierce-looking, we could not be treated in an offhand way. So the adults began gingerly to eat while the children gobbled the stuff up, choked and turned purple, and we had to punch them on their backs.

In short, our operation had not gone well. When eventually, one fine morning, the troops of the Third Reich did appear at the entrances to the valleys and systematically began to visit the houses, and then to burn them down as a souvenir (though they were not looking for cheeses, they were looking for us), the mountain folk decided to chuck the cheeses out of their houses. They placed them outside their front doors and gave them a little push—with a certain amount of regret, I sincerely hope. In that part of Italy the valleys have very steep, long, grassy slopes. The cheeses rolled down, jumping the terrace walls, and it was incredible how far they managed to go before breaking up. It didn't look like a mopping-up operation—rather some saint's feast day. At one point it seemed as if cheeses were coming down from every house; I hope the Germans thought that it was a new form of resistance, and that their warriors' hearts trembled for a split second. The meadows down below were all cheesy.

Rastrellamento: the experience, the very word was new. one night we had a warning that there was going to be a *rastrellamento*, specially for us. We all began to pack our haversacks in the dark, in a confusion that was very interesting; as in an ant-heap, everyone went round and round in the starlight in front of the hut: there was a strong wind blowing, it was like being on a sinking ship. I had to explain the situation to the British, and in order to find them in the hut I had to light a candle; a partisan held his hands around the flame, throwing a ray of light on my face; I was standing on a wooden box, so as to be a little higher. The British stood in an island around me; all I could make out was a tidal wave of heads; every now and then the wind would cause a face to be illuminated. They were attentive and puzzled. When I had finished, they simply said: "All right."

We spent the day wandering aimlessly around the windy mountains to the north of the camp, on rocks unknown to me. It was all very beautiful, though uncomfortable. I thought several times of the ancient Hebrews in the desert. Of course they at least knew where they were going, or at any rate Moses knew if the others didn't. In some ways I felt like a minor Moses: I had my desert, and my quarrelsome, vaguely fearful flock. I didn't have God in reserve, however. Our general direction was to the north. We returned to camp toward evening; the hut was intact. A false alarm.

It was now clear that the moment had arrived for us to leave. The thing was organized for us down in the plain. One night we walked down, and when the small hours came, we found ourselves in a truck, with (or should I say mainly without) our weapons and baggage, traveling up the Canal del Mis, along the road at the bottom of the valley. It was a humiliating business; I was in the rear, supposed to be in command of this mob, all heaped up together at the back. The engine galloped along—not, however, as though drawn by horsepower, but by a team of lively donkeys. It was *Pinocchio* once again. The engine galloped, the truck kept going, the boys in the back of the truck slept. I saw stretching out from us the bright, narrow backcloth of the valley in the first gray light of the morning. If just three or four Germans had stopped us, they could have taken us with their hands like fish out of a stream. The light made the valley of the Canal del Mis look as if it were full of water.

At the head of the canal we were deposited in a place called California; a valley made a T by running across the head of the canal; we were on the left branch, and we moved into the wooded side. In front of us were sheer, bare slopes, marked with roads like ribs; where the meadows ended there were arrayed the peaks of Croda Grande and the Pale di San Martino. We scattered among these woods at the foot, then sent a small patrol to explore the ridges and high plateaus to our rear; the patrol stayed away some days and returned exhausted. There were six feet of snow up there, often it was a question of walking up to the chest in snow; we would have to hang on another month perhaps, and meanwhile we were in a trap.

We had the feeling that we were looking at the world from underneath. On the slope in front of us German vehicles passed; some of them stopped, officers got out and observed us through field glasses for a long while. It was as though there was a kind of diaphragm between us and them; the idea of firing a few shots (they must have been over half a mile away, and much higher) seemed totally absurd, as if the bullets would hit a barrier of unbreakable glass and come ricocheting back.

The officers observed us; they appeared to be curious but detached, as though studying marine creatures in an aquarium. My companions kept still; all at once Bandiera pulled down his trousers, and getting down on his knees turned his bottom upwards, toward the mountain. One by one the others imitated him; nobody said anything; I alone remained where I was, seated on the ground like a shepherd with a flock of bottoms, looking up at the Germans who passed around their field glasses with calm gestures.

In point of fact we were by now virtually intermingled with the Germans; at one moment we were there, in California, at another they were. On reaching a place, one always had the impression of uniforms disappearing among trees.

One day a Communist detachment arrived at California. They were marvelous. Tattered, hurried, energetic, confident; there must have been about forty of them; the majority marched up in file, the rest came singly. They had some weapons, not many but good ones. One man was carrying a heavy machine gun on his shoulders and three others followed him with the ammunition boxes; they wore red handkerchiefs around their necks, their shoes were broken, their faces looked gay and fierce. There were young men and old men, some strong, some weak, but together they made an obviously vital entity, a Band, recognizable as such at the very first glance. They got their camp going at once, just before darkness fell. It was not a formal camp; in a trice they had put up tents, occupied a pair of cowsheds, placed the machine gun at the crossroads above the village, dished out rations and mounted a system of guards. All was very haphazard but it worked. They came from quite another area; on the way they had disposed of a German truck. They were heading east the next morning, and were counting on bumping off some more Germans on the way; then they planned to come back, or perhaps they would go on, or maybe they would even go down to the plain or up into the high Alps. They improvised according to their needs, they improvised everything. They had no pre-established plan; one day they were fighting here, one day there. We were bowled over with admiration; we felt, just on seeing them, that this was the way to conduct a partisan war. They must have picked it up from the Slavs, I thought; now we have got to pick it up from them. But how? Naturally, their human material was more suitable than ours. There were some typical jailbird faces among them; I recognized that cast of feature from roughnecks I used to see in my *paese*, people accustomed even in peacetime to settle quarrels with the knife, to creeping around by night, to burglaries and housebreaking. But among them there were others who had the faces of ordinary working-class people, people normally pacific and tranquil: it was obvious that they were all being swept along on that same impersonal wave of energy. Deeds beget deeds; one thing leads to another.

Antonio was with us; he had come to make a kind of on-the-spot investigation. I wanted to say to him: "Toni, look. *They* are real partisans"; but I didn't dare. Three of us set off with Antonio, to meet the *comandante*. Two armed men went ahead to warn him. After a while we saw him, surrounded by military figures, coming along the path; he was a youngish, robust, rather jaunty man. The word *comandante* was written all over him. He wore officer's trousers, a leather belt, and a red kerchief. He was neat, relaxed, jolly, cordial.

Antonio was dressed carelessly; he had his usual diffident, reserved manner; he looked like a hiker. The *comandante* advanced smiling, two yards away from us he halted and with his left fist in the air said gaily: "Down with Fascism." He vibrated with health, energy. Toni was a little embarrassed and said: "Pleased to meet you; my name is Giuriolo," and gave him his hand in his own curious way, with the fingers clenched. Two styles, both marvelous; I felt contradictory crosscurrents of admiration.

High on a spur on our side of the valley, Bene, Lelio, Nello, and I watched the smoking ruins below and discussed the ethics of rebellion. The Communists had gone and within hours the Germans had made these ruins. To involve poor people, one of us said, is a little too easy; everyone plays his own game, said another, one plays the rebel, another plays the German and burns the houses. We were beginning to know these poor houses and the people who lived in them. Their food consisted of polenta and in the center of the table there would be a dish of wild chicory from which everyone helped himself. It was awful to see them burning, those houses. Lelio said: "We'll have to go right up into the high mountains, where there are no people." Our Altipiano, north of Vicenza, is just like that, high mountains.

Then came the crisis. The Bellunesi muttered among themselves; for days we felt that they were hatching something, and finally they told us: they wanted to go and steal copper wire from the depots at the power station. They didn't want to *damage* it, the power station; they only wanted to steal this wire. "But why?" we asked. Not that I thought that copper was worthless stuff by any means; as a child at home I had often stolen copper things, to try to sell them at Checco the ironmonger's, and I have always had a very high opinion, probably exaggerated, of the value of copper. I was not indignant at their proposal, discouraged rather; Bene was totally against it.

"After all, we did steal those cheeses," said the introspective sergeant.

Excitedly we explained the difference between a patriotic nutritious theft and a real one. Deep down, however, I was uncertain. Mazzini had said: "Their gold, their weapons, their houses are yours if you care to get them." Presumably this applied to copper also. I decided that if they wanted to do it, I was not going to stop them; but naturally we'd have to part company.

"If this is the type of war we intend to wage," said Bene, "then count me out."

"But what's wrong with it?" asked the extrovert sergeant.

"We must try to make war on Nazism, not copper," said Bene.

"You can't carry Nazism away."

"No," said Bene. "That's true, you can't do that." He was always very scrupulous in such discussions.

This was the split; we brought it to a head with a rather gloomy discussion, on Easter Day 1944.

I uttered the first blasphemy of my life on Easter Day 1944. We were in a little hut in the middle of the wood; we had cooked some good food, meat perhaps, and it seems to me that we also had wine. We sat in a circle around the fire, having our gloomy discussion, while the Englishmen listened without taking sides. During the afternoon, right in the middle of a speech, suddenly I heard myself saying what was unmistakably a blasphemy.

The immediate effect was one of slight disorientation, but after some seconds I felt a wave of contentment. My first blasphemy had come out spontaneously; as we continued the discussion many others followed, both short and long, simple and compound, all quite convincing and with the right emphasis; toward evening I had already made considerable progress.

So we parted from the Belluno boys, exchanging affectionate blasphemies as farewells; and they were left to their fate, which turned out to be meathooks and being dragged by horses.

After the secession there began a strange period of vagabondage while completing the arrangements to go up into the Altipiano. We were four Vicentini and two Englishmen (the rest of the British had set off for Switzerland, I think); we coasted from shepherd's hut to shepherd's hut. The people were friendly and frightened; we were the chivalrous highwaymen. The news that two partisans had been killed below Agordo reached us at Rivamonte. They were the first to be killed in this area. No hooks or horses, this time; just a burst of machine-gun bullets from the top of a truck, and a corporal and two men to perform the last rites. Then the truck had left.

We were in the piazza at Rivamonte, with our hands in our pockets; the people went back into their houses looking at us with terror in their eyes.

"There's nothing we can do here," I said. "Let's go away now; let's go up into the Altipiano."

Nello had ten lire, which he had brought from home and had kept for luck.

"Let's ask the priest to say a mass for those boys," he said.

Not that there's anybody in heaven to listen to a mass; but it's like talking aloud when one is alone, it helps.

So we went to find the priest, we gave him the ten lire and made him say a mass for them; and we attended it ourselves, then we left to go up into the Altipiano, Nello and I by train, with our false identity cards, and the others on foot, because they hadn't any papers. We fixed a rendezvous on the top of the Ortigara, calculating the number of days it would take them to get up there, and then Nello and I tidied up our clothes, combed our hair, and went down to Agordo and then to the station. With money from H.Q. we bought two tickets, boarded the train, and left like two ordinary civilians going on a journey.

After Agordo the train went downhill and turned a bend. We were on a high escarpment; the valley was beautiful. On the slope in front of us, thirty yards from the line, we saw the two dead partisans lying stretched out face downwards, side by side, their heads pointing toward the top of the slope, their feet toward the bottom. They were both without shoes and wore thick socks.

5

"*Andare in montagna*": these words were a sort of slogan for the partisan movement, "going into the mountains"—and this was what we were doing. It was in fact for the second time, but we were now going into what we considered *our* mountains and—even if the approaches were long and a bit confusing—the very act was for us something sharp and clean.

The bastion of the Altipiano rises sharply from our province, in other words the plain; should anyone in some future civil war decide to go up there on foot too, he will find that it is literally a case of "going into the mountains." At a certain point the people who accompany you simply say, "Well, so long," and they are off; there you stand right below the mountains—just one step takes you out of the plain, the clandestine shambles of the plain, and you have started your climb.

Nello and I were left alone at the foot of the Altipiano at about ten in the morning; he still had a month or so to live. We began to climb the slope humming defeatist songs that I composed, but defeatist with regard to ourselves, so as to ward off any possible attack of rhetoric. The physical sense of walking upward dominated everything. The climb was truly imposing. Halfway up there was a woodcutter's or shepherd's hovel; we saw a curl of smoke coming out of the chimney, and we went inside to ask for water. There were two men in uniform with the shepherd; they were not young, fairly seasoned in appearance, and armed. Nello and I were taken aback when they greeted us in a friendly manner instead of leaping on us with their rifles, but we greeted them back. The civil war doesn't seem to count here, I thought.

"You see?" I said to Nello, when we had gone. Nello said to me: "See what?" and I said: "I don't know." So we went on singing our songs.

Toward evening we reached the edge of the Altipiano, crossed the first woods, and met the people from Asiago who were to take us by night across the open basin where the village is and then to show us the way up into the bare mountains, to the north of the basin—for us the real part of the Altipiano. Lieutenant Mosele welcomed us warmly:

"Well done," he said. "Later tonight I'll arrange for you to be escorted inside." *Inside*, at Asiago, means the peaks to the north; and when one is on these peaks, *outside* means at Asiago.

Lieutenant Mosele was gigantic, good-natured, cordial. He was visibly glad that we had arrived.

"This is a pleasure," he said. "Before you leave, we can go together to the barracks to rescue two of our boys who've been arrested. Then you can go inside."

"Excellent," I said promptly. I felt a slight sense of panic, because I was not prepared to begin like this, before I had finished arriving. They're capable people here, however, I thought—practical.

"You take command of one detachment," Mosele said to me, "I'll take the other."

"Right," I said. I felt a distinct emptiness in my stomach; I didn't even know where the barracks were or what they looked like. I waited for Mosele to unfold his plan, but it seemed that he thought he had already unfolded it: I was to command one detachment and he the other. Perhaps he imagined that, when this decision was communicated to the soldiers, they would surrender at once.

"Mosele," I said. "Do you figure, to free those boys, we'll have to go *inside* the barracks?" This was a case where one said *inside*—even at Asiago.

"Yes, yes," said Mosele. "First one detachment goes inside, then the other. And then we'll free them."

"But won't the door be shut?" I asked.

"Yes," said Mosele. "Let's see. You can ring the bell, the guard opens it, you pull him out and keep the door open with your foot. And then we'll go inside."

"Excellent," I said. "Oh, and if the guard doesn't open up . . . ?"

"Quite right," said Mosele. "We've got to think of that too."

He was so enthusiastic that I was sorry to create difficulties like this. The sense of emptiness in my stomach was beginning to disappear.

"What if we blow out the lock with a few revolver shots?" suggested Mosele.

"One could try that," I said. "But we've got to know how the door is made. Perhaps it will be padlocked."

"Then we could dynamite it?"

"We could try that," I said.

"The difficulty," said Mosele, "is that we haven't got any dynamite. The explosives are all inside."

"Inside the barracks?"

"No, no," said Mosele. "Inside the Altipiano. We can send men to fetch them; tomorrow evening or the evening after we'll have them."

"Excellent," I said. "However, in the meantime we've got to go up to the Ortigara, Nello and I, because we've an appointment there. I hope that everything will go well for you."

"A pity," said Mosele. "I would have liked you to come into the barracks with us."

"We would have liked it too," I said. Nello had never spoken during this conversation; now he wiped his mouth with his sleeve and said:

"We would have liked that very much."

For an hour or two we chatted with Mosele about how to get ourselves organized. He wore officer's trousers and gray-green stockings, but the rest of his clothes were civilian. He spoke with zest, and one felt his motives for being a rebel emerge, as well as his ideas on the development of the war. The motives were simple: sense of honor, patriotism, military dignity. The ideas were not so much ideas as images, or rather there was a central image: the tricolor flag hoisted on an eminent point of the Altipiano, between Zebio and Ortigara, in view of everything, and us drawn up around this flag, partly profiting by the trenches of the first war, partly excavating new ones, in a kind of high "square" between the bare rocks, which the "enemy" would reduce little by little, until all that remained was the flag with its pole stuck in a heap of stones, and then the enemy would stagger up to present arms to the dead.

These fantasies made me smile; but I was secretly attracted by aspects of them. Can it be possible, I thought, that we never will have the simple privilege of *fighting*? Just two lines, we on one side, they on the other?

The romanticism of Mosele seemed to me touching, and in its way useful. All these things conspire to an end, I thought: the Italian bourgeoisie is made in so many different ways, some of it is like this, people who have the flag on the brain. You can't expect people to change their brains from one day to the next.

"I'd like your opinion on another thing," said Lieutenant

Mosele. One felt that he had the urge to confess something, and that a natural reserve had been holding him back: obviously a case of conscience. In these cases it is a duty to give advice, if one can. I told him to speak freely. He confided to us that he had not yet chosen his battle name.

"Do you think it would be all right if I called myself Red Stag?" he asked. He said this hesitatingly, but hopefully.

Nello and I cleared our throats.

"Red perhaps yes," said Nello at last.

"Perhaps Stag," I said, "but without the Red."

"I rather liked Red Stag," said Mosele.

We discouraged him gently and left him disheartened but not really convinced.

On, on, up the rugged mountains north of Asiago, to the true Altipiano; night finished and day began, and ridges and plateaus emerged into light. On one of the plateaus, between the rugged ridges, Nello and I found the first real mountain unit. They were upland people; we were supposed to stay attached to them until we were in a position to start a unit of our own. We found them in a knot of crags, among bushes, dwarf pines, and tents, perhaps two hours' journey from the Ortigara. Men dressed in British uniforms rushed hither and thither, carrying cut branches, haversacks; some were shaving, seated in front of the tents, others were dismantling or assembling weapons. All were armed. The weapons enraptured us: there was an abundance of stens, they were everywhere. It was here that we made acquaintance with this little object, which remained for so many of us the principal emblem of that war. One saw at once that it was not a toy, like certain other luxury weapons, so black, smooth, and precise; it was made of rough metal, mass produced, with no "finish," and it scattered its rounds of nine-millimeter bullets in a casual way, as if flinging a handful at a time.

These nine-millimeter bullets were an all-pervasive factor in our lives. We could use them in stens, pistols, everywhere; our pockets were full of them. Nine millimeters. Why nine? What would that be in inches, for instance? Those little oblong things contained the essence of the sten gun, and ultimately of a society at war. Like a man's testicles,* they contained the point of the whole business, and the number nine, so perfect and mysterious, seemed appropriate —even though one must admit that a human testicle of nine millimeters' diameter would be pretty tiny. We loaded the bullets one by one into the magazine, which is the long, stiff scrotum of the machine gun and contains thirty-three bullets.

Nello and I were received by a squat, thickset man, with a thick black beard, who was known as Castagna. He was one of those positive, stable, practical people of whom one instinctively felt the need. He said, almost with reluctance, like someone who finds himself constrained to clarify a matter which normally he would not touch:

"I am the one who conducts the orchestra here."

He explained the situation, especially the weapons and the equipment of which we and our future companions could avail ourselves; meanwhile he got someone to fetch a sten gun for each of us and said:

"Do you know how to use them?"

I said: "A little." He showed us the movements, then added: "It's best not to drop it when the safety catch is off."

"Naturally," I said, to show myself knowledgeable. "It could shoot you up the ass."

"Oh no," said Castagna, "not *could*. It *does*."

"Surely it depends on how it falls?" I said, rather piqued.

"Not at all," he replied.

He explained that the sten was much more dangerous on its own than in the hands of any enemy. If you dropped

* *Palle*, the same word as for bullets.

it on its butt, it would fire a shot the moment it hit the ground and leap into the air; during the leap the weight of the breechblock pressed on the mainspring and the sten reloaded itself; thus as it fell again it would fire once more, and so on and so on. The point was that this gun was balanced in such a way as practically *always* to fall on its butt; moreover it didn't shoot straight into the air, but rotated scattering its bullets like a fan, or rather in a spiral, gradually lowering the angle of fire, and describing a complete circle again and again, until the magazine was finished. In this way the certainty of being shot up the ass was practically 100 per cent.

Castagna was one of those people who speak very very slowly, and appear to take all things calmly, and never to be in a hurry; but he inspired confidence, and if his sentences seemed slow, and indeed almost lazy, the conclusions were in reality peremptory. As he spoke he gave a quiet smile, like somebody who has seen a great deal in life.

We were up on a sort of natural terrace; in front of us was a great sea of frayed ridges, thick woods, scrub, and lumps of rock. It was not what one might call a panorama; it was like being on the bridge of a ship and looking at a rough sea. The overlapping waves were motionless. It looked as though some huge rubbing agent had gone over the whole area, compressing and blunting its features. One saw miles and miles of the stony stuff, compressed, confused. On the side of the terrace there was a rim of rocks which made a parapet, and at the end a bastion where a cave opened. In the late afternoon the partisans assembled on this terrace and lit a fire in the cave. There was soup, and everyone came to take some, and they ate it leaning against the rocks.

Finco appeared at this point. He was on the thin side, with a waxy face. A beard straggled from the point of his chin, a kind of little pale yellow plume. He had a delicate voice, and quiet and civil manners. As soon as I saw him I said to myself: That's him, because I already knew he was with Castagna. He was the most feared man in the whole of the Altipiano. I went up to speak to him, with a mixture of respect and excitement. He treated me with simplicity, and we began to walk up and down on the terrace.

He had in his hand a little enamel bowl, in which he was beating an egg with some sugar, using a tin spoon. Beating an egg! The thing was surrealist, yet appropriate. Finco was attached to the unit in the only way worthy of him, namely in absolute independence: everything about him was special —weapons, diet, duties. He was a great Independent. When he had finished beating his egg with the tin spoon, he began to eat, still walking up and down with me. In the end he gave the empty bowl and the spoon to a minion at the entrance of the cave, and licked his fingers.

I saw that he wore a wedding ring, so I said: "Are you married?" "Eh, alas," said Finco. But I knew that when our *popolani* say "alas" they mean "certainly." "Have you got children?" He had three and one was on the way. Alas, they were all healthy, and so was the wife.

He said that every now and then he went down to his home by night, to see them sleeping.

"It will be a great pleasure for you," I said, "when the war ends and you can return to your home."

"I'm not going to return to my home," said Finco sadly, "when the war ends."

"What do you mean?" I asked.

"I am going to the Croce Bianca," he said. The Croce Bianca was the most luxurious hotel in Asiago. As soon as he had gone up into the mountains, he had made up his mind about this, he was to go back as a victor to occupy the Croce Bianca. This was his war aim.

In the middle of the open space we came on an empty

tin can. Finco, as he chatted, took out his pistol and shot at it; the tin jumped in the air and moved about a yard. Finco fired again, and the tin made another jump and moved another yard. Thus he used up his entire magazine, as he went on casually speaking to me, without ever missing a shot. This type of aim is characteristic of *popolani* who are good shots. I am a good shot too, but that is quite another thing: mine is a deliberate aim, that is, an acquired ability; theirs is innate, infused in them directly by the Holy Ghost at birth.

The partisans were gathered in front of the cave. Castagna assigned turns of guard duty, in a homely but authoritative way.

Excellent, excellent, I thought. This is the *popolani's* war. The light faded rapidly.

I reflected that a country, the Veneto let us say (because it's safer not to say Italy: what the devil is Italy anyway?), contains enormous reserves of energy not catalogued in books. The structure of our society is bourgeois; the *popolani* are outside it. In practice they only come to find themselves inside it when they are in prison. Or when they become seminarists. This is not a form of contribution to the common culture, but assumption into service. Prison, domestic service, the brothel, the barracks, the seminary; even in books—when they appear in them—the *popolani* seem taken over into service. No, there's no question about it, I thought: there's no common culture. And how efficient they are is perfectly apparent up here, when one sees them organizing themselves on their own. They do things more easily than we do, with less nonsense; they get some things wrong too, but in an unpretentious way, in a practical and remediable fashion.

When dusk came the partisans entered the cave, and we followed them. There was a fine wood fire in the middle, and the partisans sang. Their faces, red in the fire's glow, seemed gay and excited. They sang:

> *Years have passed,*
> *Months have passed.*
> *But in a matter of days*
> *There'll be the English, at last.*

I saw their dedicated expressions, and I was inclined to rejoice with them; we felt strong, and well provided with allies. The partisans then took up the refrain:

> *Our country is the world entire,*
> *Our faith is liberty.*
> *Our only thought—to save humanity.*

That this should be their dominant thought pleased me, it was better than Leopardi. I looked at their flushed, pleasant faces, and thought again of Finco's war aim. It seemed to me that they were but two aspects of the same program, whether under the guise of the Croce Bianca or of humanity.

Later, when I found myself alone with Nello, I said to him: "This must be *popolani* culture. They are better than us."

"They even have lights in their tents," said Nello. In fact Castagna did have a lighting system in his tent, complete with accumulators and a pair of tiny bulbs, and two or three other tents were linked up with it.

One felt that here things came before ideas, and it was a great relief.

"We ought to learn from them," I said to Nello.

"We need the accumulators first," he said; but I saw he knew well enough what I meant.

"Perhaps it would be simpler if we stayed here with Castagna," I said. "Here we wouldn't have to think any more. Don't you see that merely to *be* here is in itself a solution? Castagna is at home in this place, and he will look after everything, until the war ends. Always assuming that we live to see it end."

"When do you think the end will be?" asked Nello.

"Personally I should guess it will finish within the year," I said, and immediately I regretted this. "For all we know," I added, "it could go on for years and years, or this could even be the last month."

"It's still going to be a long month," said Nello, and I said "Yes."

It was indeed to be a very long month, certainly the longest in my life, and I think in his too.

We spent another day or two waiting to go up into the Ortigara because we were early. There were explosives to be carried and arms exercises to be done. Little expeditions went off, others arrived; everyone was self-possessed, convinced, convincing. I spoke to Castagna about both his and our plans for the immediate future. He did not have any preconceived theories. His general idea was to remove the youth of the Altipiano from the little centers of habitation in the basin to the cliffs of the rocky desert; the war could be waged according to need, so to speak, without going to look for special trouble. They knew the cliffs, the splintered valleys, the ridges, the woods, the scrub, the *scafe*, the caves; the vast, wild uplands were home ground to them. Every time the Germans came they would get rid of them; they did not need to make plans. "Plans muddle you up," Castagna said to me. "We'll see how things work out in practice." Brilliant empiricism, I thought.

I also wanted to find out a little about their ethos, but naturally there is the disadvantage that in dialect such a term is unknown. One cannot ask "What is your ethos?" in dialect. And one mustn't think that the nonexistence of such a word is just due to an oversight of our forefathers when they invented our dialect. You can twist and turn that concept trying to put it into dialect, but you'll never find a way of saying it that does not mean something quite different; and it occurs to me that perhaps the deficiency is not in the dialect but in the ethos itself, which is a fine word for using in profound speeches, but what it precisely means one does not know, and perhaps its function is really this, to mean nothing in a profound way.

Therefore I said to Castagna: "Why are you all here?"

Castagna said: "What do you mean, why?"

"Why did you decide to come here?"

"Where else do you think we should have gone?" asked Castagna.

Thus finished stage one of my cross-examination. Then I said: "And when the war ends, what do you mean to do?"

"We'll go down, won't we?"

"And what will you do when you go down?"

"We'll do some looting," said Castagna.

I assented, with a feeling of scandal not unmixed with admiration.

"And then?" I asked. "After the looting?"

Instead of replying Castagna looked at me. Finally he said: "You're students, aren't you?"

I nodded, and he said: "One's only to look at you to see you're on the posh side."

"Castagna," I said, "don't you believe we might have a go at changing Italy? Things weren't going very well before. It could even be said that we're here just because of that."

"To tell you the real truth," said Castagna, "Italy doesn't matter to me at all that much."

"But it matters to you who is in command at Canove?" For Castagna came from Canove.

He said it mattered very much to him, but that he already knew who was going to be in command there: he was. "For a few days only," I said, and he said: "Let's call it a few weeks."

"But afterward—"

"Afterward there will be a government, won't there?"

I asked him if he weren't interested in the sort of government he would get.

Castagna said: "Show me your hands." I let him see the

83

palms (because that's what is meant if you say this in dialect). He looked at my hands and put his own next to them. His weren't much larger than mine, but they were almost twice the thickness.

I had some little calluses here and there on my palms, but they were pale, recent, temporary; on his he had an ancient, dark, almost congenital crust; they were not calluses, but a mutation of the tissues.

"Do you see?" said Castagna. "Whatever government there will be, I have to return to work."

"Even under the Fascists?"

"Certainly not. The Fascists are not a government."

"That's true," I said. And I heard myself wondering aloud: "What are they?"

"Shit," said Castagna.

This was his ethos. I asked him what he would do if by some ill-chance they'd come back into power. I already knew the reply, but I wanted to hear it.

"Then," said Castagna, "we'll come back too. We'll come back here."

And so we went up into the Ortigara, Nello and I, properly armed at last; and there, six thousand feet above sea level, all alone on this great stone heap, we spent three days waiting for our friends, who were to come from Belluno. We knew that Antonio might be with them.

This peak of the Ortigara, this bony skullcap, this place where we had fixed our rendezvous, in front of the great blue ditch of the Valsugana, was something that up till now I had only gazed at as a boy from another more accessible, great mountain nearby that is known as Peak Twelve. I had looked at it with enormous excitement, it being one of the legendary places of the Great War.

On leaving Agordo, it had been necessary to arrange a meeting place in some recognizable spot in the Altipiano to the north where there are no villages; and Lelio, who knew everything about the Great War, said that there was a memorial stone right on the summit of the Ortigara. So we said: "Let's meet on the top of the Ortigara, by the memorial." Taking into account the length of time needed for the others to walk up, we worked out that we would meet on May 11th.

We had decided that whoever got there first would wait three days. Nello and I arrived on the evening of May 10th. The Ortigara is a bare mountain, you have to see how bare it is to believe it. The memorial was there all right, a sort of broken pillar, all the rest was an enormous pile of splintered rubble. Nature had provided the setting, but afterwards it must have been worked over stone by stone by the guns. There were some rusty remains of war, and quite a lot of dead people's bones. There were communication trenches and gun emplacements, in a kind of landslide as though the whole mountain had collapsed.

From the peak, five minutes' walk away, right at the end of the mountain's skull, we could see a rudimentary hut. We went to look at it; it must have been put up by shepherds, and it was a good place for us to spend the night.

Before dark came I chose a large white shinbone and wrote on it in pencil, *"Lelio, we are in the hut: northwest,"* in case they arrived while we slept. Our appointment seemed totally preposterous, in that desolation of rocks, a fragment of purism so risky as to border on lunacy; and deep down I thought: They will not come.

The first morning we went out as soon as we woke up, and it all seemed a joke. The Ortigara had disappeared; we were in a great dazzling field, very steep, unrecognizable. High up, however, I saw the memorial pillar protruding from the upper edge of this field. And above it was a turquoise lake, very beautiful to tell the truth, though a little aggressive and overwhelming. The May sun was already high.

The snow made us gay, there must have been five inches

of it, and the sun melted it with a kind of insolence. We had wood in the hut, there was an attempt at a hearth, and we lit the fire to warm ourselves, because we had spent the night partly sleeping and partly shivering from the cold, but more shivering than the other. The heat that this fire made was not much, but the smoke was really abundant: if one held the door open the heat all went out, though not the smoke. We chattered away to one another among the pungent eddies, and our tears dripped briskly on the stone floor.

I went up to the memorial to make an inspection; on my return Nello was at the door, and I looked at him. His face was all black, the fair curls looked like fine gold but all sprayed with black mist, and the lips looked redder, as though he had put on lipstick. His blue eyes seemed clearer, defenseless. He was dressed as an Englishman, I myself half and half; Castagna must have given us these English clothes, I don't remember any more now.

We talked at length as we sat in front of the fire, in the acrid, scented smoke. Nello told me what he was hoping to do when the war was over; they were serious and modest plans and I felt vaguely moved. He was in his second year at the University.

We don't know precisely how Nello was killed, for those who were with him at that time were all killed too. It happened some weeks later, on the northern edge of the Altipiano, not very far from where the two of us were now, a little below the edge, in full view of the Valsugana; it was there that his body was found; and I feel now that if I had looked at him properly on that day, when he came out of the smoke at the door of the hut, I should have realized this.

The second day, toward midday, we had gone for a tour around the skullcap, stens on our shoulders, and had stopped to look at the view of Peak Twelve. I said to Nello: "Are you hungry?" and he said: "I am, a bit"; then I began to laugh and said, "Well, let's go and make some tea," because there was nothing to eat and only tea to make. We made it in the way chicory coffee was made at home: we put the tea in a tin of water, as much as it would take, then let it stew on the fire. It ended up rather strong, but had more substance this way.

Just as I had said the words "some tea" the doves arrived. There were two of them, I think they too must have been out on a sort of tour. They came from the left and with a slight fluttering of wings landed some twenty yards away from us.

These doves began to dance about in the way doves do, as though admiring the panorama. They seemed to be saying something to each other, in their own haughty way, moving their little heads jerkily this way and that. Nello and I were struck immediately with the same idea.

I made a sign with my eyes: "Do you want to fire?" Nello made a sign back: "No, you," and in my heart I knew that I should, because I was a better shot; however, if he'd really wanted to fire himself, I would have let him. I had to try to get both at the same time if possible. Not that it should have been all that hard. In theory, with a sten it should be possible to wipe out thirty-three doves all together in a row.

We kept quite still; the fear that they would go away made us swallow hard. I concentrated everything on the aim; I lifted my sten an eighth of an inch at a time, slowly, slowly, slowly, until it was just at the right height. The sten had a circular foresight, about a centimeter across; to get both doves in this little circle was no trouble at all, the difficulty was to get their heads dead center as they moved this way and that.

Perhaps it would have been better if I had fired single shots, which would have given me a chance of aiming properly; instead through sheer greed I fired a burst.

Naturally I couldn't see anything: I simply heard the dry shots, and in the middle of them I thought I could distinguish a beating of wings moving off. When the burst was over I began to look again; there in front of us was the pile

87

of stones, and beyond was the shape of Peak Eleven and beyond that Peak Twelve, and farther away still was the sky. Around our head had formed a small cloud, very very bright, which floated up into the air; however, the doves were no longer there.

I turned toward Nello. He had knitted his eyebrows, and was swallowing again.

"Where are they?" I said.

He didn't know either. The air, for miles around, was completely empty. For a long while we searched the ground among the stones, but there was nothing, only a little iron-gray feather which seemed like a dove's to me though not to Nello, and on a chip of stone there was a scarlet drop two millimeters in diameter, which to Nello appeared like the blood of a dove though not to me.

I wanted to reproach Nello for not keeping an eye on these doves while I was occupied with firing; but he spoke first. "I'm sure you got them," he said. I was sure too, but it was a pleasure to hear him say so. Nello was always very kind; so I gave up the idea of reproaching him, and we went to make ourselves a little tea.

On the third morning I went out to get some snow for the tea, and on the crest were two men standing. Underneath them the crest was like an egg, pale and gray; in the middle were these two standing; and behind them was the blue sky.

They were half turned in my direction, with the sun at their backs; they saw me but made no sign. But I laughed inwardly, through sheer contentment, because although the one behind was someone I had never seen before, the one in front had the shape, the wooden movements, the straw-colored forelock that meant Lelio.

I shouted his name and waved my hand in the air. I thought: My God, it's marvelous they even got here; and at this point they began to wave (somewhat weakly) too. Then a surge of delight came over me, and not knowing where to begin I fired a burst into the air; Nello came out, black from the smoke, with his gun in his hand. I said: "They've arrived, there they are," and we went forward firing more bursts. We were being childish, but what I really wanted to make clear to Lelio, straight off, was: Here there are weapons, and magazines, to waste, because I knew it would please him. In a few minutes we were on the summit.

The spectacle of these two was moving enough, they had come on foot from an incredible distance; and now they were here they said practically nothing, I had to do all the talking myself. I am made like that, when I am moved speaking comes easily to me, while Lelio was the opposite, he didn't speak when he was moved, nor for that matter when he wasn't moved; he hardly ever spoke. The other was a Russian, and naturally didn't speak, though he did manage a sympathetic smile. I didn't realize then that they were both weak from hunger.

Gaily I showed Lelio the pile of dead men's bones, including the tibia on which I had written my message. He looked at the spongy, light bones with a curious expression.

"We've got weapons!" I said. "Stens, and British machine guns, and grenades, lovely ones, the sort that look like pears with squares on them."

"Anything to eat?" asked Lelio.

"Of course. And tons of explosives, and detonators in copper tubes, which one bites between one's teeth like this; and the detonators are full of acid which breaks a sort of bottle inside, and the acid begins to eat into the wire. It eats away, there are some which take half an hour and some an hour, or two, or three; when it has eaten it all up, it lets off a spring and the tube blows up."

We went down to the hut and offered them some tea. We explained that there was a lot of food down at the camp.

We got ready to go and fetch the others, Antonio and the two Englishmen—they had been left behind two or three hours away, right in the heart of the Altipiano, at the

Fossetta shepherd's hut. It was a beautiful part of the Altipiano, all conifer woods, natural stone amphitheaters, bastions of rocks.

"We're the *padroni* here," I said to Lelio.

We were walking among the pines, down a slope facing east. Suddenly we heard a crackling of branches, and a voice shouted out a challenge. We all threw ourselves down on the ground in the approved manner, Lelio and I having learned something about this on our officers' course; Nello must have copied us (he had only been in the artillery); the Russian knew everything. We were in a kind of crater. Nello and I, with our stens, crawled up to the edge to peep over. Thirty yards away were some men lying down with their rifles pointing at us, and another man half kneeling a little in front, with his rifle pointing at us too. "Well, we are nearly the *padroni*," I said to Lelio.

The probability that they were not partisans like us was not very great in that area; but I was still new and it wasn't easy for me to evaluate the situation.

"We're partisans," I called.

"Put down your rifles," replied the one who was half kneeling, "and come out one by one with your hands up."

"You put down your rifles," I shouted back, "and come out with your hands up."

For a little while we exchanged these invitations. Nello next to me caught my eye, by way of encouragement; behind us, stretched on the bottom of the crater, Lelio and the Russian stayed looking up at the branches and chewing pine needles. Then the man who was half on his knees said:

"I give you two minutes, then we give it to you."

I am a little impulsive by nature. However, I can be sensible when I have to.

"Don't let's dramatize things," I said. "Do you want us to fire at one another?"

I went out holding the sten in my left hand, far from my body, and with the barrel pointing upward.

"Don't let's make fools of ourselves," I said, going toward them; and luckily they didn't make fools of themselves.

And so we joined forces and made friends. They were with a group that had been up there for some weeks. The one who had been half kneeling was called Cocche; he was aged thirty, had tufts of beard and a rather mulish temperament. He asked me various quite friendly questions, who we were, why, and how. "Now I understand," he said at a certain point. "You are the *badogliani*." *

"That's an insult," I said. "I bet you're the *badogliani*."

"No, we're not," said Cocche. "We're the Communists."

That shut me up.

"Now come to the camp with us," said Cocche. "It's a formality, but this zone is ours."

I explained to him that everywhere was for everybody, but he said that he had these orders. I (secretly) admire people who stick to orders; however, in this case I did not see why we should be obliged to obey them too. So we reached deadlock again.

"How far away is the camp?" asked Lelio.

Cocche said half an hour.

"Have you got anything to eat at the camp?" asked Lelio.

"Of course we have," said Cocche.

"When all is said and done," Lelio said, "we can allow ourselves to go to the camp."

We went. On the way Cocche said: "Oh, as a formality we'll carry your rifles on arrival at the camp."

"Fine," I said. "And we'll carry yours."

But Cocche wanted to carry ours and theirs. I proposed that they should carry all the weapons, but without any rounds in them, and that we would carry all the magazines; I felt myself that it was an odd proposal, and at any rate Cocche did not take to it. These disputes were purely academic; we knew by now that we were among friends, it

* Supporters of Field Marshal Badoglio, the moderate, monarchistic wing of the Resistance, often suspected of reactionary tendencies.

was only a question of saving face. In the end I said to Cocche: "Listen, we'll give you the rifles, on the understanding that you guarantee to say that we gave them to you of our own free will, so that you could carry them up to camp for us. Actually it does happen that we are a bit tired."

"Very well," said Cocche.

We gave them our weapons.

"You know," Cocche said, when they had got hold of them, "I've an order to confiscate all weapons."

"Oh, go and fuck yourself," I said.

At the camp all went pretty well. Cocche had removed himself a little from the group, his companions began to walk like soldiers, and automatically we began to look almost like prisoners. Here memory plays me a trick, for I don't remember any more who the chief was, and I don't even remember the camp; the light I do remember, it was a khaki color, warm, almost orange. Anyhow, in this light we were brought up to the chief, whoever he was, and Cocche made his report, presenting us as being "duly halted and disarmed."

"The partisan Cocche," I said, "only lacks a sense of the ridiculous."

I began to give a brief report; the chief recognized the name of Antonio Giuriolo and said he was glad to hear that he was on the Altipiano, and made his apologies. Then I started immediately to defend the conduct of Cocche, because I have that sort of temperament; I said how scrupulous, punctilious, and nice I had found him. The chief asked if we would like to accept his hospitality, seeing that the meal was ready.

My memory returns again when we met Antonio and the two Englishmen, Walter and Douglas, at the hut called the Fossetta. We had brought them something to eat; they must have been terribly hungry too, although Antonio never seemed to get as hungry as we did, perhaps because he was older; as for the two Englishmen, they were as hard as nails, although gentle at heart, and—as I have often found when one becomes intimate with English people—almost feminine.

The hut was empty, bare. In the whole of the Altipiano that year the huts were unoccupied; the people naturally enough were frightened, and what was more the authorities had put out certain decrees, counting on starving us out. This was a mistake, because we already were so hungry that to starve us any further was practically impossible, but at any rate the authorities tried, and to try does nobody any harm. All the same, what the authorities said did not interest us, we just took it for granted that the huts were empty.

This hut, however, was singularly empty, there was a cleanness and a poverty about it that touched me. I felt a sort of disturbed contentment deep down inside me, as well as a physical pleasure in saying a few words of English again. Antonio and the Englishmen walked about the hut in a quiet, circumspect manner, nibbling what we had brought with us, and talking to us a little; I noted that they all spoke low.

Nello and I stood listening to their voices. I thought of what it must have been for the first Christians when an Apostle came to their house. It was like this now that Antonio had arrived on the Altipiano, with his little following, in this halo of hunger. He was not only an authoritative man, ten years older than us: he was a link in the apostolic chain, almost holy. When we all went out together on our way to join Castagna, it seemed to me that even the woods, the rocks were changed, as if seen through other eyes.

Without him we didn't really make sense, we were only a group of students in the wilds, conscientious and discontented; with him we became quite another thing. Through this man there ran the only tradition which one could call Italian without blushing; Antonio was an *Italian* in a sense that no other among the people we knew was; being near him we felt that we too had entered this tradition. We only knew a few names, Salvemini, Gobetti, Rosselli, Gramsci.

But it was enough. We were catechumens, apprentice Italians. At bottom it was because of this that we were wandering around in the mountains: we were outlaws because of Rosselli, Salvemini, Gobetti, Gramsci; because of Antonio Giuriolo. We had always known it, but vaguely, obscurely. Now everything seemed simple and clear. We sighed with satisfaction, because Antonio had arrived.

6

To THE WEST, the twin gates of Corno di Campo Bianco
and Corno di Campo Verde, beyond which man must not
trespass.* To the south, a great parapet, Portule, Zingarella, Zebio, Colombara, Fiara; and in between the en-
chanted land, Bosco Secco, Keserle, Mitterwald, Cima delle
Saette, Bosco dei Laresi; on our eastern flank, the scar of
the Brenta Canal; to the north the high belt, the galaxy of
stone,† Peak Eleven, Ortigara, Caldiera, Cima Isidoro,
Castelloni di San Marco, the last confines of the world; †
the ultimate ramparts.

Castagna's camp was beneath the Corno di Campo
Bianco; from there a wide shallow ditch descended south-
ward; it was called the Val Galmarara. We kept up some
modest liaison with Asiago and other villages of the basin,
still part of the Altipiano—the inhabited, prettiest part of
the Altipiano, only three thousand feet up from the plain.

* As in Dante, *Inferno,* XXVI.
† As in Montale, *Le occasioni.*

We who were "inside" the mountains were much higher up, for the most part between forty-five hundred and six thousand feet. Supplies were carted up part of the way by means of military roads, built during the Great War. We used to go down to meet them. One day a boy from Vicenza, who had been studying at the *Industriali* and whom we only knew by sight, jumped out of one of these carts; he was called Dante. After having chatted with him for five minutes I said to myself, with a big sigh of relief: Now *he* can be vice-commander. For I saw at once how able he was.

The actual commander was of course Antonio; I had no intention of even vice-commanding anybody any more. In this I was mistaken, because if it was true that from that moment our leader, in a military and technical sense, was Dante—especially when Antonio was no longer with us—and that to him we owed whatever energy and military efficiency we occasionally managed to achieve, so it was true that neither I nor any of my companions ever entirely stopped vice-commanding one another.

The ideal of the ordinary soldier, the simple partisan, which was so romantically attractive to me, was not at all suitable to our temperaments; we were all vice-commanders by nature.

Now our other companions from Vicenza were arriving too. Enrico and Bene appeared together; we found them one day on returning to camp. They were in the cave: Enrico was standing up and wielding a tommy gun; Bene was seated on the ground and trying to untie his boots, which were magnificent and full of eyelets and laces. As he had put on some weight, he was puffing and panting from the effort. It was typical of him to arrive a bit late; it was the way he had, part of his "war on rhetoric," his attitude of scornful negligence, of being the gentleman at war, never in a hurry. Enrico, on the other hand, was an explosion of vitality; he was the only one of us who literally delighted in being a partisan, perhaps because he delighted in everything he did: his life was full of gusto, albeit mixed with impatience. He was thin and fiery, with an untidy lock of hair which every now and then he would push away with his hand—he did this when he was nervous, but he always seemed to be nervous, impatient, and short of time, and now it seems that it was right that he should have been so, seeing that he was to die a young man.

I cannot recall Mario's arrival; suddenly he was there, big and strong like Robert Mitchum, and tremendously silent. He himself remembers distinctly that when he arrived nobody bothered to greet him. This was because he arrived with the bread. He had been given a sack of it at Asiago. He was pounced upon and plundered immediately, and for a quarter of an hour nobody took any notice of him; then, he says, we greeted him.

There also arrived, wearing a dark blue sweater and a black beret, Renzo, younger brother of one of my best friends. He was shy and slender, and you could see he was the obstinate type. He's still very young, I thought to myself. I'll have to keep an eye on him. He looked like a chicken with a thin neck. Later he came to be known as Tempesta. Some chicken: some neck.

And so the school of Antonio Giuriolo assembled in the Altipiano, our wonderful school. As far as subjects were concerned, we were well distributed: one was Letters, two were Medicine, one was Law, two were Engineering, one was Mathematics, one Philosophy. We were nine, counting Rodino, who also was from Vicenza, though I don't know for certain what he was studying; however, one morning in June—within three weeks—these studies were brought to an end by his death, just a few paces from me. I have said we were nine; with the three foreigners (the Russian was called Vassili) we were twelve. Around us were gathering various groups of youths from the Altipiano and different parts of the Vicenza district.

Some of our companions from Vicenza had not reached

97

us; for one reason or another we didn't have Bruno, Marietto, Gigi, and a few more. The best of the lot, Franco, had not come because he had a bad leg, and he found it hard to walk, even in a town; he was so valuable to us that it would have been worth our while to carry him up on a stretcher, even take him with us into action, so that he could sit on this stretcher and see what was going on and explain the sense of it to us—or even paint it, because he was an artist too; he painted townscapes, crisscrossed with reddish tubelike frames, and portraits in green. But of course the thing was impractical, and then he was so softhearted it was highly probable that, when the shooting started, he would have tried to stop us firing, or at least aiming properly—and this would have been too much, for we managed to miss quite enough as it was.

Those days were shrouded in confusion. We bustled hither and thither; at first it was not clear if we were Castagna's guests, or simply temporarily fused with him so to speak—the question did not arise. There was a lot to do, as in a small ants' nest after rain. Many of us were often away on patrols, in groups, in couples, or singly; decisions had to be made and carried out. The day before we arrived from the Fossetta, the Asiago Fascists had come and put up a show at the entrance of the Val Galmarara; they had been rounded up, then sent home. Actually there had been a division of opinion among the captors: some were for an immediate solution on the spot, others for a reprieve—these last prevailed, as was perhaps right in a war between acquaintances and fellow villagers.

But I was not very pleased when I heard about it. They've made a mistake, I thought. There are too many local loyalties here; what we want is more radicalism.

It was in this spirit, I think, that the anti-Vaca expedition was conceived. Dante and Antonio were away. I had been out all morning with Lelio and Renzo; when we returned to camp, there were partisans gathered on the terrace; they said that Gino was wounded, and was now in the cave. We entered, and there indeed was Gino, deep in a pile of straw. He had gone on leave the night before, but on arriving at the edge of the Asiago basin he had thought that a search-light seemed to be looking for him, and had knocked on the first door he had come across in a hamlet near Camporovere. By ill luck it was Vaca's house, and as Gino came from Cesuna he didn't know this. Vaca was in the Fascist militia; instead of opening the door he had opened a first-floor win-dow, from which he had discharged an entire tommy gun magazine on Gino. Since it was dark, a good many of the shots went astray, except for five bullets. Gino thought: Now the searchlight will find me. Then he decided to return to camp.

Four hours perhaps were normally needed for getting back; Gino took rather more, and when he arrived he was very tired and pale. He had five holes in him, all on the same side, a sign that the bullets were still inside him; and by a stroke of misfortune one of these holes was in his stomach. Three of the rest were in his legs and the other was in his shoulder, and they looked nice and clean. We had always heard that if the stomach had a hole in it there wasn't much of a chance. Gino was calm, though visibly sad.

Radicalism, I said to myself, as I ate my midday polenta; and I suggested that we should go forthwith to kidnap Vaca as a reprisal. If Gino dies, I thought, Vaca deserves to have his throat cut at the funeral. If he lives, we'll keep Vaca as a souvenir.

Finco promptly agreed; fifteen of us filed down, by way of the Val Galmarara. This is really rather marvelous, I thought; here we are, students and *popolani* together, all armed and all marching through these magnificent tobacco-colored ravines. These *popolani* are simple, practical, "real" folk, such as we have never been; they know exactly what to do, and without having to reflect too much about it. We have brought them this tiny bit of radicalism, and they have this wonderful fund of practical knowledge. We are in what is known as an "action," we are really taking part in one. Finco is the expert; how satisfying to be able to follow him, and to learn! I savored these ideas as I marched briskly along.

Renzo was next to me, and I talked away to him, as to a younger person, about philosophy, the connection between the cognitive and practical aspect of experience and the like. Perhaps I had allowed my temporary euphoria to take over, and I said something that wasn't bitter enough, either about philosophy, or about life, or about both; anyway I suddenly felt that Renzo thought I was blind and deluded, corrupted by age and study: a rhetorician.

Renzo gave particular importance to the headlights of motorcars. He had written a kind of short story about head-lights; I think it was something to do with how they see the road going by at great speed, like a disconnected ribbon that never ends; or maybe the story was the other way round, it was the road that saw these headlights going by and as it didn't know what they meant, it felt very ill at ease. For Renzo believed that the only things that counted were head-lights, or roads, or maybe a jet of water; he thought that to bother about anything else was superficial.

Part of my energies during the partisan war was taken up with coping with people like Renzo, Lelio, and Mario, whose special brand of antirhetoric was so obstinate and so instinctive that my own in comparison appeared cold, academic, and ultimately frivolous. One felt they were anti-rhetorical because of their hormones, not to mention be-cause of complications such as headlights; the whole business made me uncomfortable.

I said to myself: When the war ends, I mean to reflect deeply on the nature of rhetoric; but now we are marching on Vaca. When we were halfway along the road I said to Finco: "How are we going to do this?" and he replied:

"Two of us will go ahead unarmed, they will enter his house and ask for water, then they will capture him."

"But what will they capture him with?" I asked, with the deference of a disciple.

"They'll have revolvers in their pockets."

Hesitantly I suggested that they should enter with their revolvers already in their hands, but Finco said no, revolvers in their hip pockets.

"All right," I said. "Who will go?"

"I shall," said Finco. "And one other."

"That will be me," I said at once. There was little choice. I was happy, and excited too.

We skirted the wooded cliffs of Monte Interrotto, which overhangs the basin of Asiago. The sun was to our right. We stopped at the edge, just where the wooded area ended; down below, in front of us, there was the lovely plain with all the little villages so clearly defined on it. Finco pointed out the hamlet to me, right below us, perhaps a quarter of a mile away, and the house, which was the first; if one sent a stone rolling with the toe of one's shoe, it would go all the way and bounce on Vaca's roof. We'd have to wait another half hour; the general idea was to arrive there at the very moment of last light. We sat down on the ground.

After a while Finco put a firm hand on my arm, and I jumped. I understood that there was something important for me to see, but I didn't know where to look. Then I saw that a couple of yards away from us there was a young hare. He must have come out of a bush; he was sitting there, looking at the view.

It was a wonderful moment, the shadows were limpid and fresh, the leaves hanging from the branches were like luminous membranes. Then someone behind us snapped a twig. The hare made a half turn, and in three bounds, without any real haste, he had slipped into the bushes. After that we set off, to capture Vaca.

Five or six of our companions followed us in a semicircle, as on an exercise; far up on the slope, two other platoons were in support. Finco and I went down with considerable agility: that swelling in our hip pockets was not a scarf, not a pair of socks, but a black pistol, pregnant with nine-millimeter bullets. The path led right into Vaca's yard.

We were twenty paces from the yard. I felt a bit of a bully, but when you have to do a thing you've got to go through with it. Finco said: "That's the door to the left." The rough wood door was shut. We were now ten yards away, still walking with a good rhythmic step; then I said loudly, warming up to the part: "I think I'll go and ask for water in this house, I've got the devil of a thirst." Five yards away the door was thrown open and out came a man with his eyes on the ground and a worried expression, and behind him were three others, also worried. I opened my mouth to say good evening, and as in a play each of these four men lifted his tommy gun and fired.

Nobody before had ever fired at such close range at me. The light was really beautiful: to the right the last clear gleam of the setting sun; to the left some festoons of cinder-colored and dark blue shadows. Things were etched delicately in the air, and the rose-colored stone slabs bordering the path like little walls (always beautiful in any light) were indeed superb, and all was impregnated with that dim, soft, mild light.

This thought flashed to me: The one in front must be Vaca; but luckily we think of all sorts of things at the same time, and while I thought this my muscles had already done something else, a kind of flicker, and I was no longer on the path in front of the tommy guns but lying down on the ground behind the slabs of pink stone; and Finco's muscles had gone through the same reflex action, with the same lightning precision, because there he was too, lying near me on the ground.

When the pink stone of the Altipiano is splintered it goes into minute pieces and sends out little powdery sprays.

Finco said: "Quick!" We made off, partly running doubled up, partly on all fours, along the line of the pink stones. The tommy guns continued to fire.

A wave of joy came over me when we reached the top of the path. Our friends who had been in support were gathered there, and we went off with them in open order, running up the slope. It was getting dark; the shots went high.

That joy was a pure joy, although there was not so much to be happy about; the "action" had been a flop. I felt like someone who has been violently massaged. There is no doubt that empiricism is like this, I thought; empiricism is not heroism. Heroism is better, but it is not really a form of life. Empiricism is a series of mistakes, and the more the mistakes the more you feel you are growing, that you are alive.

We stopped halfway up. Lelio said to me:

"I was on your left, I had the trump card in my hand, but I didn't play it."

He still held it in his hand; it was the Canadian grenade. There was no recognized technique in this war, one had to improvise. Even he seemed happy, although he had forgotten his trump card.

Now there were stars, everything down below seemed quiet; Finco walked in front of us, with his hands in his pockets; after a few hours of marching we got back to camp. Gino did not die; some of the bullets came out in due course, the rest I think are still inside him.

At the end of the war I asked about Vaca. I thought: If he has survived he must be pretty frightened by now. I felt a generous impulse to go and visit him, to reassure him a little, and to speak of that evening, to get him to explain things, how they seemed from his point of view. But there was no need; Vaca was clever, we realized that on the occasion of our visit. Some time afterward, when I was no longer in the area, he had decided to resolve once and for all the problem of how not to be captured by partisans, by simply going and joining them; and in this way he'd qualified to take part in anti-Vaca expeditions himself, so to speak.

When I was told this, I was scandalized. I felt cheated, because I had made a personal enemy of this Vaca; but when I thought it over, it seemed that our own position was not so different from his after all. We too had first been Fascists and afterward we became partisans; and it had been precisely the same with him. At the time our expedition seemed to me one of the most useless actions in the whole of the civil war; but if we take into account the subsequent behavior of Vaca, perhaps it was not so useless.

The parachute drops were at Campo Gallina; this was the fountainhead of the war in the Altipiano. There we went to fetch the fabulous brens, which came down in boxes from heaven, as everything else did; they had been dismantled, oiled, wrapped in paper; all that you had to do was to reassemble them. Luckily we had Dante, who knew a lot about weapons, and he reassembled the first one practically without leaving anything out, and soon he could assemble and dismantle them with his eyes shut. It was simply because he loved weapons, nothing to do with having taken a course.

The bren is a great weapon, light, safe, precise, and of an awesome efficiency. When Dante first tried it out, he chose a little cave three hundred yards away and fired two or three bursts into it—there was something vivacious in the way the bullets rushed in and were eventually engulfed. Finco also wanted to try it out at three hundred yards. There was a goat to kill; they brought it up to the crest and tied it to a bush under a pine. Finco fired one shot only; when they went to collect the goat the head seemed intact, the bullet had entered through the eye, and the eye was like a little dark rhododendron.

The more the bren revealed its virtues, the more we cursed the Duce. Many of the Asiago boys had been in Russia or Greece and had no respect for our Italian weapons: they said that in cold weather you had to urinate on our Fiat machine guns to make them work; as for the big Breda, it did indeed fire straight and with pedantic exactness, but it was so impossibly heavy you could scarcely move it. If you had it on your shoulders you would be overtaken by the Russians or the Greeks without any doubt. It weighed as much as a heifer.

We had quantities of explosives, also Italian and rather antiquated. We had in fact too much. There were great deposits of them in various caves; they had been accumulated there before our arrival. We had to think about guarding them, about keeping them dry and well aired; every now and then we carried a few hundredweight from one cave to another, to improve the general distribution.

Some of the grenades we had were Italian too; these were curious, innocuous objects which no one regarded as weapons, they were simply part of one's uniform, like puttees or cartridge belts. On reflection, it's not all that strange that a people who love fireworks, and noise in general, should have produced these grenades. Seldom in the history of civilization can such noise have been produced out of such fragile things. The elder *alpini* maintained that with a little practice you could make them explode in the hand; if you jumped on them, you squashed the explosion as though it were a mouse; once on my officers' course I saw one exploded by means of a back kick with the heel, as at football. A few hundred pieces penetrated the bottom of the foolish cadet who had done this, but they were so minute that it was not a question of multiple wounds but rather a sort of mechanical massage, almost an aluminum spray for toning up the backside.

Our military legacy, inherited from the old system, was in fact clumsy and torpid; even our new-found liberty could scarcely revive things. It was quite different with the squared Canadian grenades: one pulled out a ring and loosened a metal handle; four seconds later the small squares shaved the landscape clean. As we got up from the ground, we would take the Fascist grenades out of our pockets and spit on them.

Occasionally I felt the urge to make the more inexpert do tactics. Here a romantic factor was involved. The tactics we had learned on the course were stuff from the Great War. Now, up here on the Altipiano, we really did have trenches, literally from the Great War, complete with communication trenches and everything; so the romantic temptation to re-enact such tactics as I learned them on the course, but on the actual spot so to speak, and with real trenches, was very strong.

There is a moment, during tactics, when one crawls up to within a few yards of the make-believe trenches; the platoon commander says, in a low voice, *Fix bayonets,* and all try to stick bayonets onto the muzzles, and quite often they don't succeed—I've always thought that in proper attacks it must be awful if you can't do it. This moment in tactics, assuming that the bayonet has been fixed, is without doubt most exciting from a strictly sporting point of view; the platoon commander leaps to his feet, and the others imitate him, and all dash on the make-believe trenches shouting *Savoia!* *

This cry sounded perfect. I have never liked the monarchy, but I must say that the cry, when going into the attack against the make-believe trenches, never failed to intoxicate me a little, so much so that when dreaming of renewing

* As long as the House of Savoia was ruling Italy, this was the Italian battle cry.

these tactics on the Altipiano I felt I would like some similar war cry, so I hit on *Troia!* * which was satisfactory enough.

But a cross look from Lelio, whenever those frivolous impulses came over me, always pulled me up. So, as I stood in these real, scrub-filled trenches, and looked at the crooked line of the trenches opposite, just a mere four paces away, that urge to do tactics would gradually leave me; instead I felt a niggling sense of shame. But I'm ready to bet that those wretched chaps who had actually to face the trenches in the war would have felt something of the same sort of intoxication, though naturally not nearly as much, in the midst of all that horror and fear. Yet I did feel a sense of shame.

We also had some pistols, but not a single P.38. It may seem stupid, but to me there's no pistol but the P.38. That long, bare barrel; the angle of its butt so elegant and aggressive, its double metal joint that works so cleanly, so elegantly, and so terribly: a real modern pistol. But there were lots of us who felt like this, and it wasn't easy to get hold of a P.38. Later I came to know the partisan Natasha, who had long glossy hair that fell across her face like a curtain, soft lips— and a P.38. After we'd known one another for a while, I thought she was rather in love with me, and I asked her to give me her P.38; but she wouldn't. I remember she offered me a pine tree instead, an entire pine tree. Pine trees when upright seem huge enough, but when felled and lying down they appear simply enormous, and Natasha said that she had a wood all her own, and would have a pine tree cut down specially for me, and it would be mine; but this P.38 she wanted to keep, and she did in fact keep it. I refused the pine tree, which was a bad mistake; first because the gift was a poetic one, and in keeping with her rather sylvan character; then because one day I got around to working out how many cubic yards of wood there are in a big pine tree and I also found out how much a cubic yard

* I.e., whore.

of wood was worth—the result was staggering and the amount of money was enormous. From then on, when I walked about in pine woods and looked up and saw how much money there was around me, I would feel like laughing. I must add that I'd worked out the cubic yards as though the tree were a pillar cut with square edges, allowing for a bit of reduction at the top because it tapers to a point; that was because I've never liked making calculations based on circles and cylinders, let alone cones.

To sum up, the best pistol is the P.38.

One day, when I was wandering around with Dante and Enrico on the edge of the Bosco Secco, we saw a man coming toward us through the pines. He looked curiously like a clerk, and approached us as though he were someone crossing the street to ask the way. But when he arrived, he merely wished us good morning; we willingly returned this greeting. There was a lovely warm sun and the Bosco Secco vibrated with life. The Altipiano seemed practically ours; I don't know what Dante and Enrico were feeling, but I thought: This part of Italy is free. The man wore a British military pullover, rather too small for him, and seemed to be about thirty. He carried his tommy gun in an essentially non-martial way, much as one might carry a brief-case, and I noticed that stuck behind his ear was a pencil.

"Where are you going, sir?" I asked him.

"Don't call me sir," he replied. So I said, in a less formal tone: "Are you going far?"

The man made a vague sign with his hand. He said that he was with the Communist unit that operated in the area to the east of us—in other words Cocche's, without any doubt. I didn't make any comment. He said he was called Simeone, it was his battle name; he too seemed to be rather independent, like our Finco, a *vice-commissario* perhaps. He already knew about us, and that was why the encounter was so quiet; because usually at this period meeting people from unknown units invariably meant quarreling over questions of precedence.

We spoke of the various units which were in the area. This Simeone appeared solicitous and conciliatory.

"There's room for the *badogliani*, too," he said at one point.

"Certainly there's room," I said, "but where are the *badogliani*?"

"What!" he said. "Aren't you under the Campo Bianco?"

"Yes, we are," I said. "But I haven't seen any *badogliani*. However, we've only been here a short while. Perhaps they're a bit farther up."

"No," he went on. "When I said the *badogliani* I meant you."

"Listen carefully," I said. "We are not *badogliani*, indeed we are Badoglio's special enemies. Badoglio is a *carogna*." *

I explained to him clearly my views on Marshal Badoglio and his various colleagues, also on the King-Emperor and the Prince of Piedmont; and I added a footnote on the infant princes. "Therefore," I concluded, "if you put out this nonsense that we are *badogliani*, we will say that you are Trotskyites. Do you know who Trotsky was?"

"He was a scoundrel," said Simeone.

"Wrong," I said. "He was the creator of the Red Army, the best of Lenin's colleagues. He was about as good as Lenin, and still more brilliant."

"You are not Trotskyites too by any chance?" asked Simeone.

"Of course," I said, "the Trotskyite wing of the *badogliani*."

Simeone gave me a hard look, then began to laugh.

"You see how ridiculous we are becoming," I said.

"You tell me who you are," he said; and for a moment I

---

* Scoundrel, or a piece of carrion.

thought I might say deviationist Croceans of the left; but then I told him that we were students, and whom we were with and why.

"All the same Trotsky was a *carogna*," Simeone said when I finished.

"Yes, now he is a *carogna*. I don't think they embalmed him as they did Lenin. Incidentally, have you ever seen a *carogna*—a decomposing horse for instance?"

"No," said Simeone.

"One should," I said. "So I'm told at least."

"I've seen a decomposing mule," said Simeone. "It was at the bottom of an escarpment in Albania. There were lots of escarpments and at the bottom of this one there was the mule."

"Did it have its legs up in the air?"

"Yes," said Simeone, "it had fallen down to the bottom of this escarpment, and it had its legs in the air."

The following day I met Simeone again in the same place, on the edge of the Bosco Secco. I pretended to be there by chance, and he too looked as though he just happened to be there.

"What did you think when you saw this mule?" I asked him.

"Think?" he said. "What do you think I thought?"

"How far down was it?"

"Ten yards," said Simeone. "There was nothing to think about, except the stink."

"Was it a Greek mule, or an Italian one?"

"Strange you should ask me that," said Simeone, "because as a matter of fact I do know. It was Italian like us."

He had run into a unit of *alpini* artillery; while talking to some of them Simeone had mentioned this dead mule, and an *alpino* artilleryman who came from Poleo had said: "It's my mule," and had told them the whole story.

"He was called Romano," said Simeone.

"Was he a corporal?" I asked, because I knew a corporal from Poleo.

"No, the mule," said Simeone. "This mule was called Romano. The artilleryman was called Vanzo. He spoke very well of this mule, and I could see that he was as upset as if it had been a relative of his. He was an antimilitarist."

"Vanzo," I said.

"Romano," said Simeone. "When he saw a senior officer, he turned his back and did rude things."

"Kicks?"

"Noises. And when he heard the national anthem he had diarrhea. Vanzo said the same thing happened to him too." It was the Colonel's fault that Romano died. The Colonel was standing in a clearing, with all his medals flying in the wind, and the unit came up there on the path. When Romano arrived and saw the Colonel, he began to turn around and make his rude noises. At this point the stones moved, the path crumbled, and Romano slipped. The slope was very steep. He was carrying the 75 howitzer, and the weight made him roll. "He rolled then stopped, rolled then stopped; it seemed as though it would never end; he went on rolling for a quarter of an hour."

"You said the escarpment was only ten yards long."

"Yes, but he came down the other side; it would have been half a mile long, that hill. Vanzo told me it was terrible to see this mule rolling down, still alive at every turn, and not being able to help him. He swore like anything."

"Vanzo."

"Yes," said Simeone, "and so did the others in the battery."

"A horrid death," I said.

"Yes," he said. "It was easy to have a horrid death there. The crows would come and peck you. Have you ever seen a dead man being pecked by crows?"

"No," I said.

"One should."

111

"I can tell you another poem about this—about a dead man being pecked by crows," I said.

"I saw quite enough in Greece," he said. "Including Vanzo, as it happens." Three days after they'd met, a Greek grenade exploded. Vanzo was right on the edge of the crest, and he fell on the wrong side. No chance of going to fetch him.

"And I had already thought of going to find him at Poleo, after the war, to hear about this mule," I said.

"No use," said Simeone.

"There are no mules up here in the Altipiano," I remarked just to say something.

"No," said Simeone. "No mules."

Then he asked me what sort of partisan war we had in mind, and I told him with some pride, and he nodded his head. I asked him what his people's aims were, and he said: "The same." Then we said good-by and he went on among the pines, with that look of a clerk. We met again two or three times; he was always alone, as though he were going around to inspect the Altipiano, and I finished by considering him as a kind of mysterious inspector of our conscience. Because I had no doubt that the sort of partisan war he had in mind was the right one, and so long as we wanted the same thing I felt reassured.

When Antonio judged that the right moment had come, we broke away from Castagna. We saw clearly now that their approach was too exclusively local for us to be able to continue together; and Antonio did not mean to try and alter it against their will. In contrast to the rest of us, he was in no doubt as to what in general we should do: he had a clear conception of what was basic in the whole business, and in moments of crisis he never hesitated. Those were the days when people were escaping from the latest call-up, men were coming up to join us from everywhere. But Antonio didn't want them unless they were really convinced partisans; once or twice, at the most critical moments, he even made a speech, forcing himself to speak in Italian instead of dialect, so as to give gravity to what he said. These speeches are among the best things that we remember about him. With extreme simplicity he concentrated on what the people themselves wanted, and we saw that he believed that only in this way could anything constructive be done. "If anyone feels he wants to be a partisan—that is, to take up arms—because he believes it to be right, then he will not be alarmed by what he finds here, the hardship, the risks, and the fatigue. If anyone does not feel in this way, then it is better that he should go away; there is no shame in that; but he must not pretend to be a partisan; we have no place here for someone who pretends." There was something solemn and simple about this attitude. After Antonio had spoken we knew that those who remained were the true partisans.

As an antimilitarist, Antonio did not regard the war very much as a technical problem; he was totally indifferent to the kind of grenade throwing and shooting we might resort to, and he disliked rigid programs. This was not because he meant to rely on chance, or fate, but because he believed that what was really important was that the attitude of the people should be the right one, and that the rest would follow.

Should we go in for a series of small coups, or risk everything in one large action? Specialize or expand? For Antonio such dilemmas were of little importance. When important matters did crop up, matters that affected a partisan unit as distinct from a rabble of deserters, he intervened with authority. He had an arm in a sling, because when dismantling a revolver he had let off a shot and it had passed through his hand; he was not at all embarrassed by this somewhat unheroic wound, and didn't try to make it sound worse through sarcasm, as certainly we would have done. "What a nuisance it all is," he merely said to me. He had

113

had this hand with a hole through it for almost a month.

"Just think," he said. "It's a month since I last washed my face." This made me laugh and he was annoyed, so much so that I had to say: "But it was only a conditioned reflex! It's like when one hears a bad word. They brought us up like that."

Antonio said: "Yes, you're right."

"Anyhow," I said, "do you think I've washed my face much in the past month? And what about Bene—I shouldn't think he has washed himself more than twice during the whole of this month."

Antonio began to laugh and I thought: I wonder what a laugh really is. Perhaps his has something to do with the hole in his hand; but I didn't dare say so. We spoke a little about Bergson's essay on laughter, and I said: "Do you know, when Bergson died I wrote an idiotic and ignorant article about him? I think I'll be ashamed of it for quite a while."

He said: "You're right to analyze what you've done, but at a certain point you have to stop."

I said: "I think analyzing oneself is one way of analyzing the world. I feel I don't really like the world."

"You're too whimsical," said Antonio. "You'll get over it."

"If there were a good anarchist party," I said, "perhaps I ought to have joined it."

"Don't talk rot," said Antonio.

"There are some moments when I can't bear society," I said. "Hypocrites."

"You'll have to get used to it," he said. "Don't be sentimental. The world is there, and it is what it is."

"I'd rather it were different," I said. "I'd like to go on staying here, in a sort of way."

"Rubbish," said Antonio.

We hardly ever spoke about things like this with him. He stood a little above our personal problems and day-to-day life—with his arm in a sling, his clear blue eyes, his face reddened by the sun. He was a well-set-up, sturdy man; everyone called him the Captain; he didn't carry weapons, only a pistol, the one that had made a hole in his hand.

He tended to isolate himself, to walk alone, as though he wanted to reconnoiter the area. Sometimes we went with him on a sort of general staff walk, and then we would speak of war and politics, as well as literature and philosophy, or rather their history, because Antonio spontaneously turned to the *history* of things and avoided abstract disputes. He was a quiet Italian. He played down things which we were inclined to dramatize. When we proposed relatively dramatic things to him and he gave his assent, they didn't seem dramatic any more, but sensible and reasonable.

It was not his fault that, as soon as we were organized, there was a *rastrellamento* and we were destroyed. There were thousands of Germans and Ukrainians that day, there was nothing to be done; neither the terrain nor our number was suitable for carrying on any kind of mountain warfare in this part of the Veneto, except to form ourselves into a particular band, and then be exterminated. We did not think then that there were alternatives, we took it for granted that there was no other way of making war except to expose ourselves to this kind of suicide. Perhaps it was true after all, perhaps there was no other way, someone had to go through this experience. Those who were left were able to learn.

This is the heart of the whole adventure, its very center. The period was brief, a few weeks: the calendar says so. To us it seemed extremely long, perhaps because everything counted, every hour, every glance. In the face of a companion waking under a pine, in the movement of the eyes of an Englishman leaning against a rock, we could see an entire experience of thought and emotion; and we can still recall it all these years later, with the same clearness and complexity, the same absence of time. There was no time, the rocks had drunk it up, and what happened both by day and by night was without dimension.

We wandered around the cliffs, singing defeatist songs, carrying loads, losing ourselves in the mist. For a mist came up every now and then, thin and luminous.

There was no time for contemplation; we were in a whirl of fleeting images and had to sort them out in a hurry. We felt the horrid pre-eminence of having to do things—the stores, the marches—and getting on with the war. Do, do, loathsome word.

I sighed for the Very lights over Valmorbia.*

> *A ray blossomed on the stalk, dim,*
> *it cried in the air.*

Before going to sleep on the ground, I shut my eyes so that I could see these lights, then I went to sleep, and dreamed of lunar foxes.

> *The clear nights were all dawn*
> *and carried foxes to my grotto.*
> *Valmorbia, a name—and now in the pale*
> *memory, a place where there is no night.*

No, it was not like this, not at all; the dwarf pines were there, deformed by the darkness. Night did fall. It fell violently. The face of evening swelled up, like someone who was becoming angry, and went dark; then, suddenly, it was pitch black. We did not have lights in our tents, nor for that matter did we have tents. We had ground-sheets, but only a few; often four people had only two between them, then we would put one on the ground and lie on it, huddling together on our sides, trying to cover ourselves with the other one. More often than not we would wake up in the morning half buried in snow; strangely, it was not the cold but the sun that woke me. It is very odd to wake up

* A valley in the Dolomites, and a World War I poem by Montale (*Ossi di seppia*).

with one's face in the snow; at first one cannot open one's eyelids and there is a brief moment of panic. They were May snowfalls, rapid and ephemeral.

There were now thirty of us, more or less, and in the end we were thirty-six; until we came to the Fossetta, toward the end of May, the unit varied every day. It was being formed, and when we were thirty-six the formation was complete. There were other units not far off, Castagna to the south and to the west, the Communists to the east; in the mornings one sometimes heard them shooting. There were partisans all over the place, but we had to face it that there was more Altipiano than partisans. The place was empty, a desert. "I really do feel as though we are in the Thebaid," I said to Lelio.

This business of the Thebaid was noticeable in every phase of the war; but here in the high mountains we felt it all the more. It was the best place to isolate us from Italy, from the world. We had meant, originally, to be political agitators, to act and to fight; but it is now clear to me that we also wanted to withdraw from the community, keep ourselves aloof. There were in fact two contradictory aspects in our idea of a partisan band: one was that we wanted to face the world, get ourselves ready in some way to battle against it; the other was that we wanted to escape it, withdraw from it as though in prayer, renounce all its vanities.

Now I see quite well that what we wanted above all was to punish ourselves. The ascetic, rough part of our experience meant this. Confusedly it seemed to us that somebody must at least *suffer* for what had happened in Italy; in certain moments it seemed a personal exercise in mortification, in others a civic duty. It was as though we had to carry the weight of Italy and its troubles; and this was appropriate because it so often happened that we were literally carrying things. I have never carried so much in my entire life: flour, explosives, enormous cooking pots, cases of incendiary bombs, ammunition. The loads were grotesque. Up on top there would be the cooking pots and kettles, ropes, folded pieces of parachutes; then underneath, between a structure of butts and barrels, the great layer of sacks of provisions; next the swollen haversacks, full of socks, jerseys, and bullets; and underneath the haversacks, us. I had given up any attempt to keep my limbs balanced in a rational way, by exploiting—as one should in carrying these absurd weights—the structure of the skeleton, which if properly exploited will consent to carry hundreds of pounds without any special effort from the muscles. Instead I held up everything with the *pure* force of my muscles, I felt my center of gravity escaping from me in every direction like a frightened bird. I wanted to set a good example, seeing that everyone had to carry a great deal; but unfortunately Bene, who marched behind, decided to tease me and asked: "Do you think that there will still be hermetic prose after the war?" And I started to declaim against this type of prose, and Vassili, who was marching next to me, began to laugh at this excited voice issuing out of the sacks and cooking pots; then Bene and I began to laugh too, my muscles collapsed, and my load and I finished up in a heap.

There was a feeling of being involved in a really deep crisis, a crisis much deeper than one caused by mere politics.

It was not so much the downfall of our institutions, and of the wretched ideas on which they rested, as the instinctive doubt about the ultimate nature of that which lies behind all human institutions, the very structure of man's mind, the idea of a rational life, of a civil partnership. We looked on the war as the ultimate test that would throw a crude light not only on the phenomenon of Fascism, but on the human mind, and therefore on all the rest—education, nature, society.

118

One must remember that the collapse of Fascism (which took place between 1940 and 1942, in the sense that after that time it had *already* collapsed) came for us to seem like the collapse of our own cleverness, of clever young scholars and students, the collapse of our minds. Now one saw clearly how misleading it is to trust in one's own strength, to believe oneself safe. I honestly think that any Italian who had an ounce of sensibility must have felt something like this. We could not blame Fascism for our own personal disasters: that was too easy; and then it seemed naïf to believe that with the removal of Fascism everything would be all right. What is Italy? What is conscience? What is society? We looked instinctively for the answer to these and a thousand other questions, which the war unluckily could not provide. Everything seemed to be in knots, and these knots would come out in the combing. What is courage? And sincerity and even death? But that's not the end of it: What is love? What is woman?

Nonsense: one can't ask war what woman is; I did ask it that two or three times, but I never had a reply. The fact is that we saw the knots coming out in the combing; we felt that even behind politics, the queen of all these things, there were obscure forces which politics could not control. And Fascism was perhaps connected with these dark forces. The world is a mysterious place, and one feels this much more when one has lived a good while in the wilderness.

We certainly had, in that great upheaval, a few things to hold on to, and none of them acquired at school. There was the anti-Fascism of Antonio; there were the poets, Montale, and Baudelaire, and Rimbaud, and some others: many individual poems and a great mass of single lines or half lines; there was the method that we called Crocean, and regarded as a real training in thinking; and the respect for that other method, Marxism, that we'd only glimpsed at. In the moments of greatest optimism we thought that these things would be welded together at the end of the war; the tide would have withdrawn, revealing the linking slabs, the wet rock base of the new world. But these moments were rare. After the war the chaos might be cleared up, but meanwhile now we were in the middle of it and this chaos was too confusing. On every side we could see a real world manifested, infinitely more complex than the ideas put over to us by the philosophers and poets. One felt at once that this world was *real*; but how was it made? How big was it?

When the cuckoo called—because in the Altipiano they call in May—we were not there as spectators, tourists, who listened just for our own pleasure and then went back to hotel dining rooms, to telephones, to ordinary things of life. We lived there in the woods, with these cuckoos; they were real things to us and not just wonders of nature.

Once I stood alone on a boulder in the woods and began to daydream, because in the woods inevitably one ends up by daydreaming—perhaps this happens whenever one is alone: shapeless thoughts roll up slowly and continuously, they mean nothing, yet seem to carry the sting of truth. This must be why we praise solitude.

So, as I stood daydreaming on this boulder I asked myself what a wood is. There are times, I thought in a kind of free-wheeling way, when things are seen more clearly out of the corner of the eye, or five thousand eyes, or fifty thousand or even more. That's what perception is. These eyes, my mind ran on, most likely are one above the other, overlapping, the total superimposition one can call—what? —a wood maybe—that seems a good enough summary— one can also call it man, this branch of *homo* that we are, that has come out of the wood—ultimately the human brain and the wood are the same thing—and in society we have reproduced the wood and the brain, and all that is in them must also be in society.

My thoughts went on and on. There are no special conclusions in daydreams.

Yet what was important to me was the fact that deep down I felt I had understood the meaning of a wood, and because of that I remember standing there. I also remember it because immediately afterward I fired my sten. I realize now that, in that month on the Altipiano, every time a shot went off I was greatly impressed, especially if it had anything to do with me personally.

A pile of rock right in front of me, at the height of my knee, was moving. It consisted of half a square yard of greenish blue stuff, in lumps, about two inches thick, and very very slowly it moved. After a while I saw that it was a mass of vipers. They were all tied together, entangled, but loosely; they moved like those spiral advertisements which seem to be shifting yet do nothing except revolve on themselves; and roughly speaking this is what the vipers were doing. Every time a loop attempted to slither slowly out of the tangle it was slowly sucked back. After a while I was able to make out the drowsy heads of individual vipers, and this increased my sense of horror.

I thought of getting hold of a big stone, knowing that it would be easy to squash quite a lot of them, but then I reflected that it was not a very good thing to chuck stones at vipers, they were such incalculable forces that one did not know what might happen. So I put the sten at rapid fire, and in three circular comprehensive bursts sprinkled the tangle with bullets, and in the circle I inscribed two or three times an oblique cross, like a multiplication sign. The gliding and the slithering were accentuated a little, but that was all, and after I had exhausted my magazine I went away covered with gooseflesh.

Moves, transfers: they were exciting days. There was a feeling of gathering violence when we looked toward the south, and it was electrifying. May 25th was the very last date for the call-up; the Fascists and Germans had made it quite clear that after that date they meant to comb the mountains for renegades. A German airplane came and machine-gunned the wood as a dress rehearsal. Dante told me it was a Messerschmitt 210; he knew everything about airplanes too. We were in the place known as Zingarella, that day, at the back of Monte Zebio. At night it snowed.

All was a confusion of moving, halting, and moving again; when we moved we felt caught up in the war; as soon as we halted we felt back in the desert. For some while recruits continued to arrive. We were followed, so to speak, by the messengers of normality, crowds of people of whom many, too many, we considered unworthy. Career officers came—indeed I should say officers by vocation; they joined us, tasted the hard diet of carrying loads, of sleeping on moss. At the beginning they seemed to think all this might help them in their careers; then, suddenly they gave in, in the middle of yet another move, unloaded everything among the pines, and went on leave again. Then some of the ones who had professed themselves willing to endure hardship noticed that there was danger involved too. "But it's *dangerous* here!" they would exclaim, and we got rid of them. And when we got rid of them, we naturally kept their weapons: so we had these to carry as well.

Perhaps they are the normal people, I thought. What a madhouse this so-called civilization is.

After a while the recruits stopped arriving; now we were climbing toward the north, toward the stark bastions of the Alps. Every march was an adventure; we crossed new, silent, beautiful places. Occasionally scout or liaison patrols, consisting of two or three men, would be sent forward, and would be away for some days.

It was raining in the woods. Lelio and I found a little cabin made of tree trunks and covered with branches; inside it was like being in an oblong cubbyhole. On both sides there were planks which formed two beds, and on the ground was a rough fireplace. When we arrived the place was uninhabited, but there were some bundles and a kettle and various other things lying about. Toward evening two men arrived; one was old, the other of indefinite age but younger. They were civilians; we were amazed to see them there. They spoke our dialect with the Altipiano inflection, though not very marked.

"Are you rebels?" asked the one of indefinite age.

I said: "Are we rebels, Lelio?" and Lelio said: "Sort of."

"And what about you?" I asked.

"We're *mugari*," said the man.

Mugari: people who pastured animals among the *mughi*? Italy is full of surprises. The *mughi* looked too wild for pasturing.

"What are *mugari*?" I asked.

"People of the *mughi*," said the man.

Did they cut them? What did they do with them?

They lit the fire and on it they put a pan filled with what they said was coffee; then they put water to boil in a caldron (the water was in a gasoline tin, for despite the rain there was no drinking water locally), and from under a bunk they pulled out a haversack of corn meal and began to make polenta.

Then they produced two enamel bowls with blue rims, and poured coffee into them from the pan; they offered one to us, and kept the other for themselves. Each of them in turn dipped a slice of polenta into this coffee (barley and chicory), taking great mouthfuls. Lelio and I began to do the same.

This was the supper. "That's better," said the older man. The younger man said: "Usually in the evenings we eat cheese too."

"We finished it yesterday," said the other, "and the flour is almost finished."

"What happens now?" I asked.

"We go and get some more," said the younger man.

123

"Where do you get it?" asked Lelio.

"From Lusiana," said the man, "from our homes."

"Will you be going down on foot?" I asked.

The man laughed and said: "Well, we won't be going down by carriage."

"How long does it take to get down?" I asked.

"Seven hours, because we don't carry loads. It takes ten hours to come up, and it's much more tiring."

They kept up this sort of life during the summer months. They worked at the *mughi* about twelve hours a day, one week for all the seven days, the week following just for six. Every fifteenth day, on the Saturday evening, they went down to Lusiana, and on the Sunday they returned with their load. That would be their day of rest, once a fortnight.

"I prefer the Sundays when we work," said the younger man. "On the Sundays when we rest it's more tiring."

They both had families, at Lusiana; one had four children, the other three.

I brought the conversation back to the *mughi*. I didn't even know they existed, the *mughi*, before coming to the Altipiano. They had fascinated me immediately. They were not real bushes and they were not trees; they were an outcrop from the rocks on which their forests grew, almost as high as a man; they seemed soft, but were in fact very tough, and when one tried to pass through them it was as if one became caught by an arboreal force—almost liquid. The *mugo* is a vast, intricate shrub, alive, a creature which broods up there like Leopardi's *ginestra, contenta dei deserti*.

"What exactly do *mugari* do with the *mughi*?" I asked.

"They cut them, don't they?" said the man.

"For firewood?" I asked.

The man laughed and said: "Don't you know about charcoal?"

They explained everything to us. The difficulty of the

124

work, and how laborious it is to cut the *mugo*, which is not hard, but terribly tough; it was like cutting a car tire with a hatchet. And how much did they earn? I don't remember the figures any more, five came into it, but perhaps that was the number of hundredweights that a *mugaro* could cut in a day, and there was a ten or a twelve, and that must have been how many lire they got for a hundredweight, or daily. I know that they thought it good pay, and were rather proud of it; it was almost as much as a teacher's, except of course that they could work only part of the year. What seemed awful to us was the brutal, shameful form of the job: a man had to devote all his energies, all the hours of his day, all the days in a season, to accumulating these hundredweights of *mughi*, and he had to keep himself alive to do it.

This aspect meant nothing to the *mugari*. We felt we were seeing the depths of Cisalpine poverty; instead, they went on about the discomfort of having to interrupt their work by going down to collect flour, and about the trouble they had with the hatchets. Every now and then these hatchets broke, because one has to hit the *mugo* very hard to cut it, and if one misjudges the angle, the hatchet breaks, not the handle but the iron head; for even the most expert *mugaro* makes a mistake sometimes, and the hatchets have to be replaced and brought up in the sacks with the flour. The day you break a hatchet you have to work for it.

At nightfall they would return to the cabin. They had one candle, and on that evening they lit it—but usually they tried to save it. As soon as dark came they went to sleep in those bunks, and hardly had night finished when they were up and dipping polenta in their coffee and going out to cut *mughi*.

They only did the work in the summer months. This year there was the danger of rebels, of Germans, and of ending up by being shot, and thereby losing the season; but for the moment they were carrying on.

"And what do you do for the rest of the year? What sort of work?"

The replies were not clear, but I believe they meant to say they were unemployed.

In the morning (we had slept on the leaves underneath the bunks) the *mugari* made coffee, gave us some, and a little polenta, then went away.

Outside it was raining no longer; the first sun had appeared, and the day was fresh and luminous. I stood at the doorway and looked at the wood. Lelio, who always took a long time getting ready, was fiddling with the straps of his pack.

"Lelio," I said, "this may seem something special, what we have been seeing, something unusual, out of the way, but I don't believe that it is unusual. There must be masses of Italians who live like this."

"I know," said Lelio. He always knew everything.

"This nation of saints," I said, "of explorers, of poets *
. . ."

"This nation of *mugari*," said Lelio.

I was feeling very indignant, in spite of its being so early in the morning.

"After the war," I said, "if anyone forgets these things, we ought to give him a jolly good whipping."

"That wouldn't get you anywhere," said Lelio.

"In a manner of speaking I meant," I said.

"I know," said Lelio.

By now he had almost finished his endless preparations, and was combing his hair with his hands. The wood looked as if it had been washed, and it sparkled; we went away, thinking of these two Italians, and after a while we had to

* The quotation is from one of Mussolini's speeches, one that young Italians knew by heart.

enter the *mughi*, and it took some time for us to find a way through, because as I have said the *mugo* is elastic and seems to snatch hold of you.

It was during these weeks that the landscape of the Altipiano got such a grip on our minds. In the beginning, we were the more affected by its more lifeless features, and those that were inanimate or in some way, even, deformed; but having lived there awhile, and having slowly acquired a measure of confidence and strength, the very scene seemed to change. Gradually its living, thrusting, more attractive features gained the upper hand, and soon they triumphed, and took possession of us.

The real shapes of nature are shapes of the mind. One hears of such things in literature, but when one actually experiences them for oneself the revelation seems quite new. It was up there, for the first time in our lives, that we felt ourselves really free; and thus that landscape has ever since been associated with our notion of freedom.

We were on a plateau, a high platform, and all the geographical features were *above* this platform, well away from the plain, elevated, isolated. This we felt strongly; we were *above* Italy, embattled.

There is a great richness of specific shapes on this platform; it is a self-contained world, with its own mountains, its own little plains and woods and slopes and hills; it is a world between three thousand and six thousand feet high, comparable indeed to that in which we normally live, but empty, bright, shining. The most typical features, especially in the center of the Altipiano, where we were, are the little circles, the natural theaters into which the rock has modeled itself—I suppose there must be some good geological reason for them, but anyway there are a very great number, some minute, some huge, but always within human range, like ancient theaters in Sicily or Greece. The pasture is sparse, the rocks underneath are in huge slabs, occasionally visible; the upright stones, pearl-colored and pink, stand in semicircles around the little meadows, while the slabs that show overlap in regular blocks, looking like steps, terraces, pedestals, pieces of fallen columns.

In such apparently artificial surroundings even gestures and footfalls acquired shape and form in an ordered and harmonious sort of way; it seemed as if the world not only contained us but was also looking at us. Sometimes, when I came to one of these theaters, I sat down on the deserted steps, draped in moss and grass, and stayed there, measuring the little scene with my eye, gazing as far as the next outcrop of rock, beyond which there would be another, similar theater, empty; and beyond that theater there were still more theaters, in long, (to me) invisible sequences. It was like finding myself in the ruins of an abandoned city; distances were measurable, and I felt perfectly at my ease, but at the same time I was elated. It really was like being in a city, enormous, empty, and unknown.

As I say, we felt free up there; and it's not very surprising that these circles, these woods, these outcrops of rock should in a sort of way have passed inside us, into our very minds, and that we should still think of them as being a part of the most beautiful landscape we have ever known.

The boys from Roana—one of the seven *paesi* known as the "communes" of the Altipiano—made up a kind of corporation, almost a clan, since they were all brothers, cousins, in-laws, or school friends, from the same small village, namely a piazza and a couple of streets. They relied instinctively on one another and thus came to form a small, serene, compact army, organized as two complementary platoons.

They put the name of their village into their songs (the refrains used to go: *Roana, sei bella!*), and this impressed us. It seemed that they were there just for the love of this jewel of a village of theirs, and that they had no other desire but to go back and contemplate it after the war.

> *Tommy gun on shoulder—loaded with bullets—*
> *Always well armed—I have no fear—*
> *When I have conquered—I will return . . .*

They regarded us without any suspicion, but also without any special admiration; there was a sort of alliance between us. They trusted us and we trusted them. Others of our companions came from different villages of the Altipiano, but they came individually, or in very small groups; these we got to know better as persons. I became friends, above all, with Moretto, who was of my age and from one of the hamlets to the north of Asiago, right on the farthest edge of the green basin. He had left school at ten or eleven perhaps—which would be normal enough—but it was obvious that if he had been able to carry on with his studies he would have been as smart as any of us. I find intelligence more impressive when it is native and untrained; there is something both attractive and moving about it. I was very fond of him, and he of me, I think. I liked just speaking to him, not trying to teach him things, though when we talked I did find myself explaining matters sometimes, such as, say, how mountains were formed—in very general terms of course—just as he might tell me how certain plants or certain animals behave after rain.

I was very careful not to show off about being educated when I spoke to these boys; indeed I felt myself completely uneducated, and a great deal of what I had learned was a matter of embarrassment to me. But with Moretto I didn't feel any embarrassment, the question didn't even arise, we were just friends. It is strange, thinking back about this friend of mine, that I don't remember much about him in detail, only that he was dark-skinned and dark-haired, well made, vivacious and kind. When he was found, he was lying on a rock with his weapon—he died on the same day as Nello; at the last minute, so as not to be captured, he had jumped from a crag, and the Ukrainians—because there were Ukrainians in that sector—hadn't bothered or hadn't managed to get down to him, to remove his shoes and his weapon. The death of this friend of mine is not a cause for grief to me, just sadness. The sheer horror of these things can be plotted like a diagram; one doesn't feel the horror any more, it becomes a sign, a curve between two Cartesian axes, legible and painless. He was awarded the *Medaglia d'Oro.*

I do not know how Vassili the Russian came to be attached to the others when they arrived from Belluno. He was from Kiev; he immediately inspired confidence, and in fact was very able indeed, though modest and reserved. Antonio spoke to him in Russian, and this did not surprise us: how could one be surprised when he had kept himself so faithful to the realities of European history? I hadn't known before that he could speak Russian; but when he began to chatter with this man in his own tongue, and the Russian replied, it all seemed quite natural. Antonio was one of those people who speak all languages with the same accent, quite the opposite to someone like me for example, who has instead a tendency to speak them in a somewhat frivolous manner, exaggerating the most refined sound effects. Instead, when Antonio spoke to anybody, it was impossible from a distance to distinguish whether he was speaking in Russian, English, or our own Vicentino dialect, except that it *always* seemed Vicentino dialect; but on coming closer, one realized what he was up to and heard the people he was talking to replying freely as if he were a fellow countryman.

At first I spoke mostly in German with Vassili. He knew it a little better than I did; I mean his German was more down to earth than mine. I for my part knew more of the finer and abstract words. However, Vassili soon learned quite a lot of Italian; he spoke it in his own way, but fluently, and certainly he understood everything, almost as if he were one of us.

Just fancy, I thought, this fair-headed chap is a Russian, *a Russian*. He was the quietest man in the world, but in that wide-awake, live way that I have since noticed several times in quiet Slavs. Sleeping in the open, finding wood, finding water, all seemed to come to him easily. He found his way infallibly; when we had been zigzagging through the woods, for a whole day perhaps through all sorts of complications, blind marching as it were, he would remember everything, and when we had to return he would go straight back, guiding us as confidently as if we were wandering round Kiev. We recognized—not only in this—a different culture to ours, a culture better harmonized with woods; often we felt that it was basically right that he should be a Russian, but we wouldn't have been able to say why. All the same we never asked him: "What are things like in Russia?" It seemed such an idiotic question.

When there were matters to be frightened about, it seemed to me that Vassili simply didn't possess the capacity to be afraid; it wasn't that he was unaware of danger, though, only that we saw that he didn't have any sense of fear. So one day (he was shaving) I asked him: "Haven't you ever been afraid?"

"When I was small," said Vassili. And he told me how he had been to a puppet show, the sort where the puppets dangle from strings; one of the puppets had a long beard and a big knife, and was looking for a hidden child whom he wanted to kill and eat. "This one with the long beard was called Piotr."

I asked: "What was the child called?" and he said, "Vassili." I laughed.

"I was small then," he said. "Now I am bigger."

I stayed there a little longer while he finished shaving.

"Doesn't it sometimes seem to you that you are still on the end of a string?" I asked.

"That's just an idea," he said.

"It's something that I couldn't help thinking," I said.

"It's a mistake to think," said Vassili.

He is right, I said to myself, if he had thought of strings he would not have escaped from that German prison camp.

Then we got ready to return to the others, and I asked him to recite me something he had learned when he was little, and he recited a Russian nonsense poem; I listened to him attentively and then we came to where the others were.

We went on climbing, farther and farther away from the south. We walked mostly in the woods; when we arrived at each little clearing we would pause on the edge to have a look, almost as though we were eavesdropping; often in the silence we would hear the distant roarings of bombardments on the plain. "That would be Treviso," we would say, "and that Padua." Sometimes we went ahead to reconnoiter, in twos or threes or fours. Once, when I was on a reconnaissance patrol with Dante, Lelio, and Enrico, we reached a clearing and saw that there was a hut in the middle of it. This clearing was some fifty yards in diameter; the place was beautiful.

We peered out cautiously through the trees, and waited a fair while. The door of the hut was open; the sun was as hot as in summer. Finally Dante said: "Let's go and look," so we went—or, rather, ran—across the clearing, with a curious sense of exposure.

Inside the hut there were signs of a hasty departure: odd shoes without soles, empty tins, rags, straw, bandages. On the stove there was something which seemed to us incredible: an earthenware frying pan, the bottom covered with a veil of gravy, in which lay a piece of congealed meat.

Evidently the Communists (there weren't any other partisans apart from them between us and the Valsugana) had made off in a hurry, and this made us feel that we wanted to be off in a hurry too. We were rather upset, partly because of this almost summerlike, deadly silence, partly because of the sight of the meat.

"The Communists eat meat," said Enrico, and he added one of his blasphemies which were theologically atrocious, but so charming that I don't think anybody in Heaven would really have minded.

Lelio took the frying pan; we doubled back across the clearing and into the wood, then we sat on a rock with our legs dangling over.

"We could divide it into four bits," said Enrico, looking at the meat.

"It must have been cooked several days ago," said Dante.

Lelio sniffed carefully and said: "It doesn't smell at all bad."

"Should we divide it into four parts then?" Enrico asked. We tried to pull at the stuff with our fingers; but it was not meat but sinews, and could not be separated.

"It's best to eat it as it is," said Lelio. "Otherwise we'll ruin the taste of the gravy."

The meat was in fact covered with the thick, orange-colored gravy. I put it in my mouth and chewed five or six times. It tasted good. Then I passed it to Lelio, and he gave it to Enrico, and later Enrico passed it to Dante.

The thing was indestructible, so we passed it around a second time. At the end all that remained was a pile of white ox sinews. Dante wanted to throw it away, but I put it in the pocket of my tunic, and that morning I chewed it several times more. Then we went on reconnoitering the wood. There was nobody about, we were still alone.

Hunger was constantly with us, but it didn't get us down; it was a cheerful sort of hunger. I know what real hunger is because I know people well who have known it well, especially at Auschwitz, and later at Belsen too, where it was still worse, but they say that by then they hardly felt it at all. They don't talk much about this hunger, or indeed about the whole experience, but strangely one understands it all the same; these communications come in a very curious way: almost nothing is said, and at a certain point one understands almost everything. Our hunger instead was not real hunger, only a great desire to eat, and there was a great scarcity of food. There was maize flour and margarine, which of course was rationed. The flour was cooked with water in a parachute drum of black tin. This polenta tasted of varnish; at first it was pretty nauseating, but in the end the flavor became so familiar that polenta without it would have seemed insipid. When it was cooked this yellow slime, streaked with black, was ladled out with wooden spoons into mess tins and other containers. We did our best to behave in an orderly way, huddling around the drum with our knives clutched in our hands. But when the last spoonful had been dished out, we all pounced on the drum and began scrabbling at the crusts inside it.

We used to mix margarine with the normal ration; this was delicious. There was also another way of eating polenta with margarine, a very recherché way: we put pieces of tepid polenta and margarine on the top of a can, then we placed the top on the embers, and when the polenta exuded an oily liquid we ate it.

At first, we occasionally had bread to eat too; we would march for hours to meet the villagers bringing it up by night to some appointed place; then back we would march with knapsacks bulging, throughout the remainder of the night. But after a while these supplies ceased. And we had no more news from the villages either.

However, some very exotic foodstuffs continued to arrive from the air, always by night, a kind of modern manna, more beautiful than good to eat, as I have always suspected was the case with manna in olden times. There were some rolls of a strange product called "bacon," composed principally of salt, and some tins of a pale smooth paste which tasted of nothing and which was Canadian cheese; and there was the egg powder. This last was not at all appetizing; when it first arrived we were standing there looking perplexedly at the package, and Lelio and a boy from Roana took heart and began to eat it with their hands. Lelio just ate one handful, then stopped; the boy from Roana ate all the rest and after that drank a mess tin full of water, because his mouth felt like dough. Then he began to feel ill, and the others started to make him drink more water to revive him. When he went into a coma, I read what was written in English on the package: "Powder of highest concentration. One hundred eggs of Canadian hens. Mix with water for requisite volume."

The boy from Roana was more dead than alive. Everything depends on the speed of fermentation, I said to myself. It was in fact a race against time; at one moment it seemed that we had won, at another the fermentation. The boy from Roana recovered, but afterward one only had to say "Cluck, cluck" for him to pass out.

We now went in the direction of the Fossetta hut, and finally in the last days of May arrived there. We settled ourselves partly in the hut and partly on the spur of tree-covered rocks that overlooked it. All at once it struck me that the unit was formed, ready. Suddenly we felt we were weak no longer, but strong. We were exactly three dozen; it seemed a perfect number to me. Our equipment was excellent: we had two brens; the chaps from Roana had one, and the English the other. The two English boys held theirs in high esteem; when they first saw it they smiled with satisfaction, and took it into their care almost with affection. Walter told me the names of its various parts in English, and I remember how interesting I found the word "safety catch" for *la sicura*. We no longer thought about *rastrellamenti*.

This is the moment, I said to myself; now the war has begun. I explained my ideas to Antonio, that we must get going at once, go down into the plain, improvise: a sabotage, a little dynamiting on the railway, a little machine-gunning of a German vehicle. Act first, then learn your lessons, I said; and Antonio in his quiet way said that he agreed.

The first "march of aggression," toward the Valsugana, was more of a demonstration than anything else. We carried explosives with us to blow up the railway at the bottom of the valley. We knew that the distances were very great, but one has to try them out to discover how really great they are.

We marched in double file, all strong men and healthy, well armed, optimistic. The passive phase is over, I thought; now we start. There was a late afternoon sun, everything was efficiency and energy, Antonio was with us, we were a magnificent unit. I believe I had even combed my hair.

At the Fiara shepherd's hut, within view of the little hidden basin called Marcesina, we stopped for a while so that we would have the right light—for we knew that the slopes overlooking the Valsugana were bare and without any sort of cover. We were dispersed around the hut, and were all smiles as we leaned our haversacks against the outcrops of rock; I chatted with Antonio about war and poetry. In the whole civil war I don't think I was ever so happy.

The last bit of the Altipiano, before one comes to its tall eastern edge, changes character dramatically. The country is completely clear of forest; to the south of Marcesina one walks in an area that is almost meadowland, between hills whose sides are smooth and absolutely naked, incredibly attractive. The surrounding shapes are simple, clear: it is like some marvelous fairy tale where everything is simplified, big, amiable. We walked in the middle of this fairy tale, as though between high, taut, painted curtains: the clarity was such that the scale of the mountains seemed enormous; and suddenly coming out of the wings there was the edge.

The edge was a shock: just a line—a big jump into the Valsugana, one mile below. At our feet another curtain of steep meadowland fell away downward some hundreds of yards; its draperies were simple and pretty, lightly gathered at the foot of a row of rocks and boulders overhanging the violet crack of the valley—which is the deep narrow ditch through which the Brenta runs.

Here you really understand how the Altipiano is made: the great, smooth, pure shoulder divides it off like a world apart, and from this point you see at a glance how high and remote it is. It is not really surprising that, in all the years since, when I am half asleep and thinking of the most perfect place where I'd like to be, I always return to the top of this shoulder, to one of those little stone huts dotted about on it. I imagine myself lying in wait by night, with two or three of my companions, for the *rastrellamento* convoys—complete madness from a military point of view, naturally, but this dream of perfection of mine is not military.

When we reached the edge on that occasion, in the half light, we knew immediately that we were not yet halfway: the entire night would not give us enough time to get down to the bottom, and to find ourselves down there at daybreak with the whole unit, in that narrow trap between such sheer walls, would be lunacy. We needed long preparations, supplies brought up by installments, staging points; in fact the whole unit ought to be returned to base, from which small groups could be detached.

So we waited there, in a hanging wood, and spent the night shivering. Toward morning Enrico said:

"Let's two or three of us at least go down to Enego and do something, now that we're here."

"But what can we do?" asked Bene.

"Oh, things outlaws do," said Enrico.

"Let's all three go," I said.

"I'm coming too," said Dante.

There was a doctor to bump off in Enego, the first of a long series of doctors and pharmacists with whom we had to deal in one way or another. "Bump off" is a manner of speaking. We were only going to kidnap him. Antonio hadn't even warned us not to harm the man, he took it as understood. However, I thought deep down: If anything awful does happen to us, the doctor will get it in the neck too, but I didn't say so out loud.

The affair was pretty risky. Enego must be twenty-five hundred feet high, more than half a mile below the edge where we stood; the distance along the road was about six miles. It is a village midway down the slope, with good access to the valley, and had a large military garrison. Our name was already familiar to this garrison though in a distorted kind of way. Some game warden on the Ortigara had found the tibia bone on which I had written my pencil message for Lelio, and had misread the name. He had brought down news of this "Zelin," who subsequently was made out to be a captain with a band of men up there, and who received messages on bones of dead men. Apparently there were still people of this ilk who went up into the mountains in the middle of May, game wardens, frontier guards, and so on; I imagine that as the year progressed the desire to climb up there passed.

And so we four said good-by to the others, and went slithering down the dark, meadowy slope.

Some shelving fields, a fair stretch of very steep woodland; on coming out of the wood we saw a small church, and around it some houses. There were five houses in all, and there were fifteen families; but I had no time for sociological reflections. The place was called Frizzón, a *frazione* of Enego. We were the first partisans to have come down into that particular zone; they treated us as if we were their sons.

We sent someone to fetch one of Bene's school friends who lived at Enego. He came right away, and they brought him to us in the little wood where we were, not far from the houses. He was called Sergio; he was less than twenty years old and terribly excited. "So it's true," he cried out, "the partisans do exist! You are the partisans. You exist!"

We told him yes, we did exist, and he waved his hands up and down trying to express adequately that we had his moral support. At the end he found the *mot juste* and cried: "Wound me!" To tell the truth, this outburst seemed very touching to me, and I nearly did give him a little wound.

Sergio gave us all the information we needed about the Fascist militia at Enego, and about the doctor who was the pillar of the local Fascist party. This man was from southern Italy, and had done some pretty awful things to those who had avoided the call-up, and to the population in general. "He killed my cousin; he made my aunt die," the people of Frizzón told us, but it turned out that they were only talking about some wrong diagnosis, not politics. "That doesn't count," we said. "It's not part of the civil war." All the same, his record in the civil war was also quite plain. This business of carefully going over the ethical side at the last minute has always been a characteristic of mine.

Then Sergio went away. In the afternoon he wanted to make us some personal gesture, and brought bread and wine and other things to eat from Enego; he also brought a little sister aged perhaps fourteen called Miranda. We were the center of a sort of peaceful, clandestine traffic; these two, and others, came and went with news and gifts. Miranda was a brunette; she had short hair, and was silent and very sweet. She did her best to make herself useful, and one could tell that we appeared in rather too favorable a light to her. She was at that age when girls look at one moment like children and at another like grown-up women,

139

and these moments keep alternating. However, she was quite well developed and, as I say, very very sweet.

She came to me with a bowl of soup, and while her brother talked animatedly with Bene, she sat down on the ground in front of me to wait for the bowl; the ground was sloping a little and as she was sitting with her legs apart (she wore no stockings) I saw her thighs, which were very well made, and her short, tight, black calico drawers, more like a girl's than a woman's, but pretty exciting all the same.

Fortunately there wasn't much soup left; it was good, but it made me choke. I asked Miranda some silly questions as she sat there in front of me, and she would reply "Yes," or once or twice "No." Then she rose to her feet and took the empty bowl. Now I was absolutely fascinated; this girl looked as if she was alight, and everything she did seemed to vibrate. However, I said nothing, and I didn't try to speak any more.

Then some more time passed; there was some stuff to carry, and I don't know what else. I was sitting on a wall, doing up a shoelace; Miranda came along the path in front of me gathering primroses. I watched her without compunction, because I thought she hadn't seen me. But when she came right in front of me, she stopped and offered me these primroses, and I took them.

"How kind you are, Miranda," I said; but I found it difficult to speak. She didn't say anything, I got up on my feet and we were very close, and she didn't draw away. As I put out my hands I imagined the points of her breasts crushed against my chest, and I think this is what was going to happen, but that villain of a brother of hers called her, and she roused herself and went away.

We slept fully clothed; all the time that we were on the Altipiano, I don't remember ever taking off anything except my shoes. That night, before going to sleep, I unbuttoned my trousers in front and inserted the primroses, and they got scattered around everywhere inside, and for days and days I kept on losing them, first down one trouser leg, then down the other.

The next day we went down to Enego to kidnap the doctor. We had decided to kidnap him in full daylight, during one of the times he was doing his visits in his car; however, he never went up, only down, toward Primolano. I said: "Then we'll have to come back through the village with him"; and Enrico said: "So much the better." It was a risky thing, but stylish. The hillside under Enego was completely bare, so we had to lie down flat to wait for the car (which was a Fiat Balilla), hiding among the folds of the undulating meadows so that we wouldn't be seen. We were at the first turn below the village. When the car appeared, we let it come up right close, then we jumped out, two on each side, and stopped it. There were big luminous clouds, very high; it was a lovely clear day. Bene climbed in behind to hold down the doctor, Dante got in next to the driver in front, Enrico and I mounted the dashboards with revolvers in our hands, because you can't manage a tommy gun while simultaneously clutching the roof of a car. We set off toward Enego, meaning to pass through the village at great speed, and so come to the road for Marcesina; but a great speed in an overloaded Balilla climbing uphill is really no speed at all, just noise. I looked inside and saw that the doctor had collapsed on the seat, and Bene was fanning him with the palm of his hand.

Now we had reached the first houses. The people were looking and staring at us; they could see full well what we were, though apparently were not absolutely sure if we were flesh and blood or just an apparition; they simply stared. Bene waved to them from the window, flourishing his pistol in a cordial sort of way as if he were an armed bishop; then he went on fanning the doctor. Now we were in the middle of the village, it went on and on, it seemed as long as a year of famine. There was a central crossroads, a steep curve, rather like an asphalted ravine; the people were leaning against the walls, backing away into their doorways. We were above the ravine, we entered the piazza, which was large; right in the middle, as we were crossing it in that happy, festive light, the Balilla gave a big cough and died on us.

We behaved like young maestros. Dark looks, monosyllables, you here, you there. One felt at once that this was how it should be done. Dante and Enrico took charge of the piazza. I opened the door and said to Bene: "If the soldiers come, please kill the doctor, then get out at once." Next I said to the driver: "Now you get the engine going."

How sunny the piazza was, what fun the war. The light was intense, like pearls.

In front of us there rose a tower with an armorial emblem, the glorious *scala* of the Scaligeri; high on the left the church; in the middle of the piazza a monument, with a man on top representing "The Great European War." This man was facing where we had stopped; he was thin, brisk, irritable-looking; he wore a helmet, puttees, and a smart close-fitting uniform. In one hand he waved a flag, in the other he held a fistful of nuts, or wild chestnuts, or very small grenades or something, which he seemed eager to throw at somebody. I thought: Perhaps our names will end up on this very stone under the others from the Great War. Our emblem will then be this thin, nervous man with that handful of bronze stuff; he doesn't look like us, but neither does he look like the unfortunate people whose names are carved beneath his feet; he is smart, with a well-ironed uniform, they were clumsy and dirty. We too are dirty, though actually not at all clumsy. All right, what the hell —let him represent us. . . .

The driver pulled out the starter, but the battery was dead.

"Let's push it backward," I said. "And," I added to the driver, "if the engine doesn't go, I'll shoot you through the ear." I made Bene get out, and we started to push the car backward; every now and then the Balilla got stuck as it knocked against its own reverse, which sounded as if it were hitting rocks, and Bene took the opportunity of encouraging the doctor. "Don't get alarmed," he said. "We're studying medicine too; we're almost colleagues."

At long last the Balilla pulled itself together and the engine started again; the car set off in a cloud of steam, and we escorted it to the end of the piazza, then Enrico and I jumped on the running board, while Dante ran on foot by a short cut so as not to overweight it.

It seemed inconceivable that we wouldn't be followed; I was clutching the roof with my left hand and with my right I made circles with the revolver by the driver's ear, as an encouragement. Every now and then I peered inside; the doctor was still half paralyzed with terror. Bene was trying to calm him rather too much, I thought. I saw that the doctor had a rosary in his hand, and that he was furtively moving his lips. You bloody old whoremonger, I thought, you've even got a rosary ready in your pocket.

We went up the hairpin bends, climbing as though we were in a small airplane. Every now and then we looked down; Enego appeared ever smaller and farther away among the pines.

The mountains on the other side of the valley, with their little villages and all, fell away, fell away; soon we had nothing in front of us to the east, except the air, and far away the phantom of the Grappa. Suddenly it seemed that the road had become tired of climbing, and it started to twist sideways; we had entered the high zone where we were in command. Enrico, on the other side of the roof, looked at me with his fierce face; I smiled at him and he smiled back. We came across a horse drawing a cart; I shouted to our driver not to slow down and fired a shot to warn the carter that he must give way. Enrico immediately followed suit. The carter had already gone right over to one side of the road; the shots served only to frighten the horse, which started to rear madly. At any rate we passed without slowing down, and soon we were at the top, on the edge, and in no time reached the plain of Marcesina.

We halted, and I said to Bene: "Make the prisoner get out." The doctor got out, trembling. Suddenly he seemed to me just a poor, old, bigoted man, who was slobbering with fear, with this rosary twisting in his fingers.

The driver hadn't said a word except "There you are," when the engine died; he looked at us with wide-open eyes, and at me especially, as though he suspected us of being mad. I could see that he was a nice chap. Some weeks later he too came up to be a partisan, and almost at once, on a patrol, the Germans killed him.

I told him to return to Enego and go straight to the head of the militia, give him the best wishes of Captain Zelin, and hand him a message. On a page from my *cahier jaune,* which went with me everywhere, I wrote in pencil: "Dear *Maresciallo,* Today I have arrested your doctor; if you take any reprisals whatsoever at Enego, I will give orders for the immediate execution of the prisoner." I put the date and signed the letter "Capt. Zelin."

The driver left; some weeks later, it was with this same Balilla that they came up to fetch the dead partisans, of whom he was one. They put him on the roof and took him down again that way to Enego.

We marched, with the prisoner in the middle of us, to the Fossetta hut, arriving there toward evening. Antonio came to meet us; he seemed more like an alpine camper than the head of a military unit. I told my companions to halt and stood at attention in front of Antonio, saying in my best military voice:

"Your prisoner, sir, arrested according to orders."

Antonio said: "Well done, well done"; then he said to the prisoner: "Are you cold?" because the fellow was rather lightly dressed. He told him he need have nothing to fear: after the war he would have the chance to reply to the accusations of the people of Enego. The general policy of all this seemed impeccable to me.

But there were problems created by this prisoner. We had put him in the sheep-pen in front of the hut, alone, with guards taking turns. I went to explain everything fully to him. I said that he had had the good fortune to fall into the hands of civilized people (namely us), and that he might as well get the thought out of his head that we intended to do him physical harm, let alone bully him, even verbally. The doctor impulsively threw himself down on his knees and took my hands, and wanted to kiss them, and covered them with tears and dribble. I snatched them away, and he lost his balance and tumbled forward. I wanted to shout: "For God's sake, man, pull yourself together!" Instead all I said was: "Oh do please get up," and helped him to his feet. He was about the age of my father.

It's an unfair advantage, when talking to a prisoner, not to be the prisoner; I realized this and the thing made me ill at ease.

The morning after the capture of the doctor Simeone arrived at the camp, alone, with his rifle slung over his shoulder. He had come to congratulate us.

"You haven't popped him off yet?" he asked with an air of earnestness.

"No," I said.

"Does he sing?" * asked Simeone.

"I don't think so," I said, "at least I haven't heard him. At present he's praying. He's got a rosary."

"You could make him eat the rosary for a start," said Simeone.

I laughed, rather embarrassed.

"What kind of end do you have in mind for him?" Simeone asked.

* A slang phrase for "Is he talking?," i.e., "Is he spilling the beans?" (under torture).

145

"Actually," I said, "we don't have any kind of end in mind for him; when the war is over he'll be tried in the proper way."

"This business of keeping hostages is dangerous," said Simeone. "I'm not saying it's wrong, but it's dangerous."

I had the impulse to tell him that we hadn't meant to use the doctor as a hostage, at least we hadn't thought of doing so; but instead, I said: "That's what we've decided," and Simeone repeated: "I'm not saying it's wrong." Then he asked me to lend him the prisoner; he said that he would like to have him at his unit for two or three days, with full guarantee to return him unhurt, minus his ears. "There's somebody who is very keen to bite off his ears," he said, smiling. I found excuses for not lending the prisoner to him. I asked myself: Is this a marginal difference, or a central one?

My position with regard to the problem of the prisoner was beset from all sides. One afternoon, on coming back to camp, I found a group, composed of some of our people and the Englishmen, playing cards with him. I was horrified, and took the prisoner away (he was winning too); then I gathered the unit together and harangued them. I laid down a policy of absolute nonfraternization. "The Prisoner," I said, "is the modest representative among us of a thing with which we cannot have human relations of any kind; we can't maltreat him, and we can't even play cards with him."

One of the Englishmen observed that in England it is normal for warders to play cards with people who have been condemned to death, even if they are the worst thugs or murderers. I had to translate his observation to the others and meanwhile I thought of a reply; then I replied in Italian that we in Italy had abolished the death penalty when my grandfather was still small, and therefore we could not take into account the usages of countries penologically more backward. Bene, in order to embarrass me.

asked for an official explanation of the word "penologically," and I gave him a suitably obscene one. I then translated this part of the debate into English, leaving out some of the words.

There was obviously a strong current of feeling against me: I felt isolated and virtuous. I proposed that we ask the views of Captain Antonio, who at that moment returned from a walk in all his majesty holding a small bunch of red berries in his hand; and the Captain, having heard the case, announced—a bit sadly—that I was right. However, without my knowledge, he too later entered into human relations with the prisoner. I now know that one evening he went to see him, in a private capacity, and gave him his own flannel vest and, I think, his woolen pants too.

7

DING DONG BELL went the alarm. The Englishman on guard
duty came and woke us in the hut; he said: "Lots of vehicles."

It was the night of June 5th, nearly morning. I had been
dreaming that the fuse was about to blow in the Valsugana.
We had been preparing for it for days, and often at night
I had these dreams. We felt confident, and—in anticipa-
tion—pretty proud. The action had been fixed for that very
day, June 5th; for two or three days before this date it
had rained with hardly an interruption. There wasn't room
for everybody in the hut, so several of us were outside in
this rain, ground-sheets around our shoulders. We're still
a fine unit, I thought nervously. On the night of the 5th it
stopped raining.

In a moment we were all out on the spur, among tufts of
mughi and groups of sleepy people; and in the patch of
darkness where we knew the basin of Marcesina was we
could see a long file of lights coming along slowly, slowly,

slowly, in pairs. Instinctively we started to count them. When I had counted thirty pairs, I stopped. They are like beetles going two by two, I thought, each with a candle on its back.

There was no doubt that they were coming expressly for us. Behind us stretched a thick wood right up to the northern edge of the Altipiano, to the peaks called the Castelloni di San Marco and the Caldiera. Methodically we hid all our belongings, because it's not all that advisable to be attacked with a haversack on your back, then we divided ourselves into groups. I was with Dante, Enrico, Renzo, Mario, Bene, and Rodino.

Antonio headed due north with a couple of squads of men. Perhaps we said *ciao* to Antonio, but I don't remember doing so. The night was coming to an end. He went on his own way, out of my life, with his arm in a sling, into the wood above the Fossetta.

For us seven the *rastrellamento* was fairly uneventful. We turned west and walked in the wood all morning, choosing the points where there was some visibility, and where especially we could see the military road that goes to the Lozze and the Ortigara. At first it was all very pleasant, there was dew in the glades, and the woods were beautiful. We hadn't brought anything to eat with us, but after a while we noticed a great white lump in the middle of the pine branches; it was the parachute that had been lost in the last drop. We had searched for it for hours and hours at the time, and now we had found it without looking: it's like that up on the Altipiano. We cut the cords and opened the cylinder, all thinking the same thing: *Gesù Bambino*, please let there not just be weapons; in fact it did contain some things to eat, and we gave our sincere thanks to *Gesù Bambino*. We ate his health at once in chocolate and sardines; may there always be asses' milk and dates available if he has to escape another *rastrellamento* of little children by that impotent coward Herod.

From where we were at the edge of the wood we could

see the columns regrouping, forming cordons and Indian files. There were thousands of soldiers; dispatch riders rushed hither and thither; all this a few hundred yards away. Halfway through the morning I became afraid; it was the only time I really was afraid during the war. It was obvious that we were in a trap. I had always imagined that about a hundred men would attack us, or maybe two hundred; but here there were masses of them everywhere. At the beginning we had had the feeling that the Germans were in front, so at least there would be plenty of empty space behind us; but we could dismiss that idea, for firing was starting up to our rear, where our companions were supposed to be. We had now withdrawn into the wood, so we had lost the benefit of seeing the attackers; we felt they could arrive from anywhere. We had two or three magazines apiece, and some hand grenades: enough for a five minutes' battle. Dante had made us form a "hedgehog" among the pines. "This is where we stay," he said. It was at that point that I felt afraid. It was real fear, an exciting experience. It seemed so much easier to go out and meet them at once. Luckily we had Dante with us; he wasn't afraid, or didn't show it.

"What shall we do when we see them?" I asked between clenched teeth; I kept them clenched lest they start chattering.

"Just don't think," said Dante. He was right, don't think is the answer. In fact they didn't come to where we were; and so the day passed.

The next thing I remember is that we had returned to the Fossetta. It was evening and the *rastrellamento* was over; the trucks, down at Marcesina, were beginning to drive away in long files. The hut no longer existed; we paced out the length of the black remains; they seemed so incredibly small. The Germans had found some of the hidden haversacks, but not all. We didn't know what to do.

The two Englishmen had been captured, most of the

rest had been killed, but a few had escaped. We found only two boys, Vassili and another, alive. They were from the squad which had had the prisoner. All I remember now is that we were sitting on the ground in a circle, and that I asked: "Have you killed the prisoner?" and that they replied: "No." I remember snatching the tricolor ribbon off my khaki shirt, and throwing it on the ground as though to break it.

Lelio's story is strange: one of the two "captured" Englishmen, Douglas, turned up a little later in the Altipiano, still in fact uncaptured. The two who had been captured were indeed Douglas and Walter, but Douglas was Lelio.

The nastiest thing about these *rastrellamenti* was knowing that we—the Italians—would not be taken prisoner. If things went badly, they went badly in only one way. One tried confusedly to prepare oneself for that moment of horror, the worst of all possible moments: of finding oneself still alive in enemy hands. Sometimes I asked myself wearily if any of the rest of us could pass for Englishmen, like Walter and Douglas. I knew the language a little, but my black hair would have inevitably caused them to mistake me for an Italian before I had the time to speak; Lelio had incontestably northern blond hair, but he knew no English, and I never thought he had a chance as an Englishman.

He was near Walter when he was hit on the head with a rifle butt, so it was Walter who spoke in those first crucial moments. When they were brought before the interpreter down in the plain, hours later, the thing had already been arranged. The interpreter asked questions, and Lelio kept quiet, and I bet it didn't cost him much effort. Walter explained that this Douglas his companion was Welsh, and only understood Welsh; the only word he knew in English was *fochinau*; so Lelio with his Welsh identity was taken to a camp for British prisoners, and then to Germany, and he remained there all during the war, saying *fochinau* every now and then, and after the war he was repatriated to England, and finally he returned home with some packages of rather sweet cigarettes, and brought us the good wishes of Walter, and told me that English newspapers (contrary to what we had imagined—a really *free* press!) are not in fact very interesting, except for the letters they publish from members of the public which are a bit better than the rest of the stuff in them, but not much.

The rest of what happened on that cruel spur, above the Valsugana, where Nello and Moretto and so many other companions of ours were killed, I have never wanted to reconstruct. I know various things, and they are very honorable, and even legendary. But I do not want to speak of them. Antonio did not die there, on those gloomy crags, but far away, far from our life, not pursued by Germans but in open battle, which was more appropriate.

And so June 5th ended.

There followed days of rain, of damp mist floating in the air, of dripping pines; off-balance days. It was all a bit upside down: we spent our time lying in a crooked, doubled-up sort of way on the slopes; the landscape was distorted, the tent which we had made out of the parachute was a crazy shelter anchored to the branches of the pines; sometimes strange bursts of laughter would emerge from us, and even when we stood up we seemed curved and distorted.

Some said that with the rain the *rastrellamento* would not continue; others maintained that the *rastrellamento* was certainly still on—but we didn't care. When we went out we looked dazedly at the white, incredible tent. We returned inside to lie curled up beneath the dripping branches.

We had flour, and plenty of water; the only difficulty was lighting a fire, but luckily we had incendiary grenades and we used one for each meal. The pines above were swallowed up by the clouds. The dominant color was a gray so pale as to be almost white, but lower down, where our feet were, all was brown and dark green. Our feet didn't seem to be our own. The flame of the incendiary grenades was really unforgettable; it began by being lemon-colored, but one octave higher, then turned to a pale, cold turquoise; and it gave the impression of whistling, of a kind of colored hissing.

There was something uncanny about the whole thing, we all felt it very much. It seemed as if there was nobody left on the Altipiano. For all we know, they may have wiped out everybody, I thought, the *badogliani*, the pseudo-*badogliani*, the Communists. And what if they were to wipe out the whole population of Italy? How funny it would be, I thought, if only we remained, eight men from Vicenza and a Russian from Kiev. Because the nine of us were all that were left. We hardly spoke, and every now and then someone would give a tired laugh. Bene said: "It's a strange moment, this; there ought to be a writer among us." However, there wasn't one, so the thing vanished into the air, and nothing remains, except the memory of that wood where it rained.

One morning the fog lifted and the sky was clear. Renzo and I went off together to the edge of the wood to see if there were any *rastrellamenti* about; we went forward a long way and finally arrived where we could see, and we looked. There were alpine pastures, undulations, basins illuminated by the sun. The countryside was sloping down, it was empty.

For a while we looked at this empty landscape, and as there was nothing more to do we stayed there for a while seated on the ground. We both felt that we wanted to say something, but neither of us knew where to begin, or indeed what to say. All at once I heard the song of the birds. It had been there before, but now I heard it: at first it seemed like a confusion of high intermingling notes, but afterward we came to distinguish the individual voices, birds calling out to each other, in their several ways. Renzo began to tell me to what birds the calls belonged; he knew them like people of his own village. Then he began to call out to them too, sometimes whistling loudly, sometimes gently hissing; he called to them, and they replied, and there I stood gaping, listening to these conversations; but after a while I got the hang of them and began to follow what they were talking about, and soon I followed them quite well. It was like being abroad, when at certain moments one forgets altogether that other people are foreigners, different creatures, and that one knows almost nothing about these creatures, except they are well made too, and can reason in their own way, and have a life and vitality of their own, and probably believe themselves to be the center of the world; suddenly one finds oneself inside a life that normally one would not consider one's own, and without really knowing the language one understands it; because to understand languages the important thing isn't just to know them.

And so we spent the morning with the chaffinches, the thrushes, and all sorts of other birds chattering away.

Then Renzo stopped and we went off, leaving those birds there, and they went on calling and calling in the woods. When you come to think of it, if you look at things from the point of view of a bird, it's a bit odd staying there all morning, making these cries among the leaves.

When it stopped raining, the rock soaked up all the water; the Altipiano dried up. We had marched the whole day toward the south with our haversacks, and were between Zingarella and Zebio; we were accompanied by a partisan from Asiago whom we had found on the way. Suddenly he said:

"I never told you that the British have landed in France."
We said: "Oh, fuck them all!"

That night, the night of June 10th, Bene, Enrico, and I went to sleep in a little hut halfway up the slopes of the

Zebio; nearby in a cave was another unit—what was left of it. We thought of making a new start from there. It was as though we had been orphaned; we kept together, like a group of people who are cold. As a matter of fact we were really cold, and we slept huddled together for warmth. Before they went to sleep Bene and Enrico spoke of the brothel in Vicenza (only one was properly licensed); they called it our episcopal brothel, because everything is episcopal in Vicenza. Then we began to sleep, but almost immediately someone from Asiago woke us up and said that a *rastrellamento* was coming; they had known in the village that this was going to happen because of the quantities of bread that had been ordered in advance for the troops. The man from Asiago was on his way to warn the people who were in the cave near us, and as he had seen us sleeping in the hut he thought he would warn us too. But whether warned or not, it was to make little difference to us.

We went down in the dark to wake the boys who were still at Zingarella. Again we hid our haversacks, then we started to walk toward the north, still in the dark, trying to get as far as we could before it was dawn. After a while we divided ourselves into two groups: Bene and Enrico with the Russian and another went to the left, the four others and I to the right on the north flank of the mountain. This mountain was called Colombara.

We chose a point halfway up, on a sort of terrace among the *mughi*. Rodino was next to Dante and said to him: "I feel I'm going to die today." The ground was very rough; all around were the scrolls of the trenches from the Great War, on one side the Italian trenches and on the other the Austrian; both sides must have been literally on top of each other. The trenches seemed minute. It was getting light.

The dawn was cold, huge, part pale rose, part pale green. We heard the rumbling of many engines; these rumbles seemed to mount toward the circle of the horizon, making it vibrate in harmony.

The first sun came and filled an interval that did not seem to be made of time.

Then everything happened in jerks, like detached scenes in a film. Suddenly there were voices on the mountain, very close, all around us. Dante slipped his identity card under a stone, mechanically the others imitated him; we all had our backs to the north and our faces toward the mountain; we were spread out along the terrace, quite still. Then to the right, a little higher up, we saw a row of young men walking with a great deal of circumspection; they were in open file and had already occupied a quarter of the landscape to our right; they wore green-colored helmets. We heard words in Italian, in dialect; the young men had an unwarlike and homely air. It was incredible that they wanted to kill us; it needed an unpleasant effort of will to be convinced of this.

I was kneeling under a *mugo*. I made a sign to Renzo behind me to take off his safety catch. Dante was to my right, a little farther ahead. The file of young men was passing a few score yards away, but we realized that there were many more, the whole mountain echoed with tramping feet. Then came the last hallucinatory moment of immobility; the branches of our *mughi* rustled, we were on our feet; the first shot; it was at such close range that the military uniform into which it was delivered seemed to muffle it. Dante and I both shouted simultaneously: "Quick! Run!"

I was wearing low city shoes, yellow ones; a few days before I had put my boots to dry by the fire, too close, and they had been burned, so as I had my city shoes in my haversack I had put these on. They were terrible for *rastrellamenti*, but the fact is that I had them on, at least at the beginning I had them, then I lost one. I decided to throw the other shoe away too. I had put the safety catch on my tommy gun, because I fell about a great deal, as I bounded from crag to crag—there's no other way of getting down quickly, excepting bounding like that at this point on the Colombara.

The first bound brought me face to face with a young man with a green helmet crawling along a terrace; his head was higher than mine, but not much; he had the frightened face of a recruit. Irritably I pointed the barrel of my tommy gun at his face, and made a gesture as if I were frightening a hen. Fool, don't you see I'm busy? Perhaps I was wrong not to have killed him. At any rate he withdrew his head and dragged himself backward, and I started bounding again. All this sounds far slower than it really was; it was like being on a merry-go-round, in the midst of a great wave of rhythmic, confused energy. There were shouts and rustlings all over the place; the shots sounded like exclamations; everything seemed to be exploding, the countryside, the way we moved; we fell down, we stood up, we were upside down, then on our feet again, or on our knees against the rocks or against the *mughi*; we turned somersaults, all mixed up with each other; now we would be far apart, now close together again. At one point I found myself between Mario and Renzo, filing sideways along a cliff, and I said: "We haven't much of a chance."

Now I was at the bottom, on a sort of plateau, practically on the level, and I was alone. I didn't notice the shots any more; I was only aware of little dry clicking noises, and of seeing the branches of *mughi* flying off in curious jerks. These noises were tiny, isolated from the rest. It seemed as though kittens were tearing all around me, with incredible ferocity, and mangling themselves in the air as they passed. I knew well enough what they were, but I was not prepared for the sense of repulsion that their speed inspired in me. I felt that each was attached to a long thread, and there was a horrid tug when they passed too close. I was right in the middle of a skein of these threads.

I headed northward, not running any more; I could hear firing there too, but far away. At a certain point, beyond

157

a low hillock, there were no more kittens, not even any branches flying up into the air. I was out of the line of fire, perhaps by thirty yards, and I was walking on a platform pleated with furrows. When I saw I was all covered with blood, I was alarmed. I thought: It'd be funny if I couldn't run any more. But I felt all right, only a bit shaken up. Then I saw a narrow crevice in the ground, and without thinking I let myself down into it. I could barely squeeze through, but underneath there was plenty of space, deeper than my own height, and oblong in shape. I lowered myself, holding on to the edges, and when I had my arms three quarters stretched out, I touched ground.

Suddenly I was out of the sun in a cocoon of subterranean rock, in a damp darkness. I heard people running above, whole platoons of people: the rock overhead was rumbling; I felt my heart rumbling too, in such a way that the two things at times became confused with one another. Now I heard voices too, very close, talking Italian. They were speaking about somebody, who turned out to be me; they were looking for me, with real concern. I was fully aware of the fact that they wore boots, and the nearness of their feet to my face was not pleasant, for I knew it was the tradition for rebels to be kicked to death. I was holding a grenade from which I had removed the safety pin; I was keeping the lever down with my thumb. I stayed still, with my eyes on the hole above where the light was whirling.

It was like playing hide-and-seek as a child and waiting for people to find you. There is a moment when everything seems to have happened already, you've been found, there remains only the formality of finding you. And so I waited in my hiding place, looking up at this crevice and thinking: Oh Christ, how alone I feel.

So the morning passed, but for a long time I didn't notice it was passing. Then I realized that the voices had gone away, the platoons too, at a kind of trot; every now and then some isolated person passed, also at a trot, but he didn't seem to matter. Suddenly there came to me the incredible idea: Can it be that they won't find me? This gave me a certain brutish relief and I felt a touch of scorn too: What clowns, I thought. They're worse than we are. Now I felt bothered at the idea that they might find me by accident, by mistake as it were; so I thought of trying to close the crevice with a stone—there was a big one on the ground. I put the safety pin back in the grenade and held it in my mouth by the handle; then I lifted the stone above my head and leaned it against the crack: it did the job almost perfectly. I remained there for a while with the stone above my head, in darkness, and with this grenade in my mouth, but suddenly I felt a fool and put the stone on the ground again. I had a little book in the pocket of my jacket, so I opened it and began to read. It was *A Sentimental Journey*, a pocket edition, the English on one side, Foscolo's translation on the other; the prose was beautiful both on the right and on the left.

For a while I heard more shots, and automatically I would think: That would be Dante. And that would be Renzo. Then, when I'd finished off all my friends, I went on reading until evening.

Rodino was killed almost at once, at the foot of the slope. He was found with his vest all perforated, and his face disfigured with kicks.

A couple of times I had tried to look outside, by climbing on the stone. I got my head to the level of the crevice; when I opened my eyes the afternoon light was quite a shock—it was like an agitated, irrational pool, out of which electrified particles seemed to be spraying. I decided to hang on until nightfall. I certainly can't stay here forever, I said to myself. You grow old underground you know, and you lose contact with society.

When the crevice became dark, I said to myself: Now;

and without further ado I went outside. It was pitch black. It was raining. I didn't recognize a thing, yet I was not worried about my sense of direction, because I knew that I had been facing north all day—it was as though I had been magnetized. Everything seemed deformed; the trees were gigantic, as though tangled up with one another; the whole platform of rock looked crumbled in upon itself, and the black sea of the Bosco Secco surged everywhere among the rocks. The *mughi* were like impenetrable islands; as I tried to walk around them I would suddenly find the rocks no longer under my feet, and down I would drop into black emptiness, my hands clutching at branches. It was a complete labyrinth of ledges, crevices, branches, bushes; only with the greatest effort could I disentangle my legs. I felt I was making no headway at all, that I was perpetually going round and round in a mad circle.

For quite a bit I went on like this; I had forgotten about the *rastrellamento*, I was only concerned with this sea, so full of rocks and branches. Then suddenly I realized I was in the open. I had emerged into more ordered country and began to walk quickly. The north was still, constant, but the south, when I tried to turn to look at it, tottered and rolled—away, away. As I walked in the rain, I began to hear noises floating around me in the dark. Some were like footsteps, or voices—but I couldn't be sure. Then, suddenly, I was sure. There they went, bloody Stakhanovites of the *rastrellamento*, night patrollers, hunters in the rain. Damned whores, all of you, I thought to myself. I stopped, put my hands around my sten, ground my teeth in fury. My hands were in the correct places, my left halfway along the magazine, near the barrel, my right on the metal stock by the safety catch. My hands were there, in their correct places—but there was no sten. It was very curious. First I noticed that there was no safety catch; then that the trigger was missing. There was no magazine, either, nor stock, nor barrel. There was nothing.

Well, that's that, I thought. So I've lost my sten. Often when we were small, at Fascist parades, we lost our rifles. First we had the little wooden ones, then as we gained in age and wisdom they gave us rifles of varnished metal; finally when we grew to maturity we had more or less real ones, the "muskets" which I shouldn't imagine killed many enemies though they did accidentally kill a few fellow boy-soldiers. We used to lose these rifles and muskets quite regularly, at the Fascist parades; we were scolded a great deal for doing this, but we lost them all the same. However, as so many of us lost them, if we looked carefully enough we usually could find another that had been lost by somebody else, and we used to hand that in.

I stood quite still in the darkness, in the attitude of somebody getting ready to fire a burst from his sten, except that I didn't have a sten. I must have left it in that damned hole, I thought. Deep down I felt a little pang of relief that Dante wasn't there—he would have taken a very poor view of such absent-mindedness.

But of course Dante will never know about this, I thought; because I took it for granted that everyone was dead. It occurred to me that perhaps other stens must be knocking around somewhere, up on the Colombara. I tried slowly to turn myself toward the south, toward the place where the *rastrellamento* had happened, not because I wanted to go back there—I had already been walking for several hours—but just to have a look. I couldn't see anything, either near or far. The southern side of the night still swayed a little, but much less. I turned again toward the north: the silent, open, black north. I let go of my imaginary sten gun; I found I had three hand grenades on me, a heavy one of the squared variety in one pocket and two light ones in the other.

I continued to hear those nocturnal *rastrellatori*, quite distinctly, but they didn't come any nearer; instead, it seemed to me that they were getting higher, as if they were climbing a cliff, but at an ever-increasing speed, almost as if they were in a helicopter. They climbed into the black air and I followed them with my face; when they were as high as a church tower, perhaps a church tower and a half, suddenly they dispersed in a rose of dim rays and began to fall. When they reached earth they were rain.

Of course there aren't any *rastrellamenti* at night, you fool, I thought; and from then onward I walked more confidently.

These were the only ghosts I met during that Monday night. Twenty-four hours later I met some more, but they were pacific, neutral ones. That was the disadvantage of *rastrellamenti*: if you were alone, you were afflicted by ghosts at night. Dante began to see them at about the same time as I did, on that same night; because Dante was alive, though grimy and bloodstained, and was also walking, but toward the south. He didn't experience my revulsion for the south; he was certainly shocked too, even though he was much more used to war than I was, but at least he did head south that night, because he knew that in a matter of hours he would reach the first group of houses at Gallio, and he was determined to get there and knock on a window. I must eat, he thought, take off my clothes, dry myself. Sleep. Toward midnight the ghosts started; they were all in little patrols and spoke in Italian. Dante stopped and they stopped, too: they stood watching one another, he and they, about ten yards apart; they were almost invisible because of the tremendous darkness. Dante could only make them out in patches, as it were—their whitish faces, the outline of their slung arms. He stayed quite still, ready; sometimes they looked like *rastrellatori*, sometimes like trees. He kept his eyes on the pallid faces, his finger on the trigger, and breathed as quietly as possible. Gradually the faces and the shapes dwindled away, and Dante couldn't see them any more. Then he thought: I've good eyesight: if I can't see them, they can't see me either. So, very cautiously, he began walking again, until he saw more ghosts behind more trees. The valley was full of ghosts, and that's why it took Dante several hours to get down to Gallio, with all these halts, and all these staring contests. But at last he arrived, knocked on a window, and it was opened; so he dried himself, drank milk, and slept. In the morning he was stronger than ever, and in fact as soon as he could, after a few days, he went up to Zebio again. There he saw the smoke coming out of a cave and he stopped to see who came out, whether it was a *rastrellatore* or someone who had been *rastrellato*. After a while somebody did come out. It was Enrico. The others, apart from two or three, were with him.

They made a great fuss over Dante, because after the first shot, when Dante and I had given that simultaneous shout, he had jumped straight into a ravine and had disappeared, rolling downhill like someone who'd been hit. So the others had taken him for dead, in fact as having literally "fallen" in a *rastrellamento*; and they had already sent the news to the family and his girl-friend in Vicenza. Now that Dante was alive they fussed over him like this, and at once sent a counter-notice to the girl-friend and the family.

Mario and Renzo were hardly shocked at all, because they had kept hidden together in a gorge. When there are two of you, you don't feel so much shock; they passed the day of the *rastrellamento* keeping quiet in each other's company—not being two who spoke much in any case. They just listened to the *rastrellatori* and kept quiet. Toward evening they left their gorge and wandered about in the twilight until they came across a handful of fellows from the other group who were fairly calm because they had been missed by the main *rastrellamento*—although all through the day Bene had been terrified of the thought that there might have been vipers lurking in his hiding place. So the whole lot went down to Zingarella, near the hut where we had hidden our haversacks. However, the haversacks had been *rastrellati*, and the hut didn't exist any more either: there was the usual sad pile of black, smoking cinders. They lay down to sleep nearby, on the slabs of rock, in the middle of the *mughi*, and slept happily all night. They found my shoes the following day, quite far apart from one another, but didn't send any condolences to my family. They concluded that alive or dead I indubitably would have been without shoes, which was true; and so for a while they didn't know anything more about me, but I don't think that upset them overmuch. I know they were fond of me, but things like that don't at the time cause displeasure, nor for that matter pleasure, naturally, they don't cause anything at all. However, my shoes weren't of any use to anybody because I had smaller feet than the others, and what was more they were rather small shoes even for me. They were low-heeled city ones, yellow, as I have explained. To me, during the few days in which I wore them, they seemed completely unsuitable, out of keeping with a warrior. Bene, on the other hand, deep down in his heart, liked things which he considered to be virile frivolities, Anglo-Saxon stuff; and I do remember that, after the war, as we watched British officers in their yellow shoes in front of one of the churches at Vicenza, he said to me: "Look, do you see their shoes? The real thing. Gentlemen-at-arms."

Rodino too had no shoes; he was only in his socks. Our friends covered him with stones, and left this pile there, and then at the end of the war some of us went up, and took away the stones, and gathered up what was left.

The ground under him looked as if it had been sown with spent bullets; because when the body disintegrates, and the structure of what was a living boy vanishes, the bullets fall out like ripe seeds; and then at the end of the war, when one carries away a few rags full of holes, with a few bones inside, these bullets are left swarming like worms on the ground.

Of all who were left alive I think I must have been the most shocked, and the principal form of my shock was my abhorrence for the south. I walked toward the north, without shoes, and after my first brief encounter with the ghosts, I went quickly enough. I was suffering from a pretty violent form of shock, and there's no question that it gave me a kind of energy. I reckoned that in choosing this absurd route back to the world I was taking on an immoderate task, but still I felt full of tremendous reserves of strength. The essential geography of the Altipiano was quite clear to me; I knew how to get to the Marcesina basin, and from there I could find my way down the eastern flank of the bastion, the split of the Valsugana, and come to a place where there were houses and men, at Frizzón. All night long I walked among crags and circles toward the north, partly on ground covered with bushes, partly on bare rock. It rained continuously but mildly, as in autumn; for hours it rained in the absolute darkness, then gradually I realized that I was beginning to see something. It was not from the sky that this change began, as happens in clear weather, but quite the opposite; it was at ground level that the dark began to yield vague outlines and dark shapes, which gradually turned silver-gray and soon were rocks, terraces, saddles, silent circles. I walked on, past these silent places, and only later did I observe how much lighter the sky itself had become, and I saw that it was full daylight. At this point I also looked at myself. I was wearing a British army shirt, the sort that has no collar; my trousers were the zouave type, all in rags. I had on two pairs of stockings, but the feet were completely worn away, and all that was left was a sort of double bandage around my ankles. My feet were white. Now I walked faster still, across the phantomlike, gray-green landscape. When it stopped raining, a translucent, glowing mist appeared, gently filling the mountainside and streaming in pale festoons among the rocks and the trees.

I now heard motors in the distance, and occasional shots; this time they were not ghosts but realities, though far away.

As I walked, sections of the landscape kept appearing in bits and pieces out of the mist and seemed to be moving. At any moment, I felt, some enemy unit might emerge in open order from this mist; I took a small Italian grenade, a *signorina*, out of my pocket and undid the safety catch. I began to move slowly and carefully, as if I were on tactics.

One of these festoons of mist was hanging over a little saddle: I felt that the enemy was there. I passed the *signorina* to my left hand; then I took the Canadian grenade in my right and got ready to throw that too, my index finger firm on the handle. Now the mist was running past me, thinning out: I could see shapes scattered about in the alpine meadow, waiting. I had raised my left hand. First the *signorina*, I told myself, then follow up with the Canadian grenade. Suddenly the countryside cleared: the mist drew back its last flurries as if they were a skirt, and I found myself out in the open, alone in an alpine meadow dotted around with pretty little rocks and some young fir trees.

I felt absurd, with my hand in the air, and the grenades. I can't go on like this, I said to myself. I'll never arrive if I do. It was the grenades that were making me behave as though I were on tactics.

I thought: The war will end, and the years will pass, and everyone will go back to their jobs, and I'll still be wandering about these woods and meadows doing my tactics. I put the pins back in the grenades. There was a tall fir tree, curiously black against the light and right on the edge of the saddle, so I went up to it and placed my three grenades at its foot. I put two on the ground, side by side, and the Canadian one on top. Then I had second thoughts. I picked up the Canadian grenade and put it in my pocket.

After a few hours I reached the dense woods to the east and entered them. A little while later, as I stood in the middle of these woods, I heard dogs rather far off, but not all that far off. I clearly heard commands being given in German, as if on an exercise. Thank God the ground began to slope downhill and soon I didn't hear the dogs any more. I knew I was approaching the basin of Marcesina, and in fact at sunset I caught sight of it among the trees, green and charming, to me infinitely touching. I moved around the edge of the wood, to find a point where I knew I could cross the basin as soon as dark came. This point is really just a big clearing with one stone building in the middle—in peacetime an inn; during the war it was an ideal rallying center for *rastrellatori*. I could see that there were no trucks, though there was a certain amount of coming and going, people in uniform and a German motorcycle with a sidecar. I let night arrive; then with great caution I came down into the open, crossed the basin, which is perhaps half a mile wide, and went up among the bare humps in front. The light of the moon was creeping up from behind the crests. The crests looked smooth and pure. I now headed for the edge of the Altipiano, and when I reached it the moon was high; everything was bare, limpid, deserted; I stepped down from the edge onto the steep slope, sliding quickly for a while; then I stopped and turned around. The meadow behind me was almost vertical, huge, unreal. In all my life I have never seen anything that looked more like a dream. I stood staring at it for a while, thinking: It's only the shoulder of the Altipiano, that's all it is; but it didn't seem a landscape of this world. Then I continued my scramble down the slope to Frizzón, and when I reached the wood I took a path which skirted it.

I was thirsty; I couldn't remember having drunk anything either that night or the day before, or the night before that, or the day before, or even the night before that—the night of the 10th. That's a lot of days and nights,

I thought. At a corner of the path I stopped. To the right there was a steep ditch full of rocks and shrubs, impassable; on the far side of this, in the shadow from the moon, I saw two huge jellyfish. They were the first animals that I had seen for quite a while. They were sitting on the slope, perhaps three yards from me, but out of reach.

They were a couple of feet apart, as though tangled up in the undergrowth, and were heaving gently: opalescent, almost transparent. I was utterly amazed, the thing seemed almost incredible. How could these jellyfish be up here? They looked tangible and real, so I was convinced that there must be some sort of explanation. I picked up some stones, and began to throw them at the jellyfish, to make them move; strangely, the stones went right through them, without making any difference, and this increased my sense of irritation and disappointment all the more. "Oh, go to hell," I said finally, and started walking again. As soon as I turned the corner I saw, in full moonlight, a small fountain, and this gave me a special thrill of pleasure because—as I say—I wanted very much to drink. I couldn't remember having seen this fountain before; indeed, it seemed a very odd thing to have built it up there, in a deserted and mountainous place, where there were no houses or anything. It was of recent construction too, quite modern in style: a small pillar made of polished, irregular stones; a good, thick jet of water gushed out from the curved spout. Why on earth have they put it here? I asked myself. I leaned against the pillar and bent toward it with my mouth open, but the pillar didn't hold me up, I went clean through it with my whole body and fell on my right side—it was quite a considerable fall, because the path sloped downward. When I'd done falling, I didn't feel any pain, but some days afterward I found a large black bruise on my hip, a little bigger than an apple and a little smaller than a melon.

I stood up and tried to walk on. The path still went downhill; it was wide and covered with sharp splintered stones. It was a terrible business knowing where to put my feet, not so much because of the pain, but because of a kind of jerk into which my feet went, each in turn, whenever I tried to take a step. I kept falling about like a drunk; now my hands were hurting too, but what irritated me most was the thought of being perfectly sober and in full possession of my senses, apart from not being able to control my feet and ankles, and apart from these infuriating, rebounding jerks. It's only a small technical problem, I said to myself, as I sat down on the sharp stones, it's a small problem, but I've got to solve it if I want to go on.

I tried going on all fours, but it was worse. I also tried lying on my side and rolling; but I rolled crookedly, and would at once find myself stranded on one or another side of the path. It's my center of gravity, I said to myself: it's incredible how many things depend on one's center of gravity. The sharp stones kept on sticking into me, all over my body, whenever I touched the ground. For a while I slid down in a seated position, ignoring the behavior of the sharp stones. Bugger you, I thought; actually it was the other way round—and anyway I was hardly making any progress.

And the moon had made a great fish-dive in the sky, its tangerine color had paled; I was on my feet, and stayed on my feet. I was walking on the road among the houses of Frizzón. I knocked on the first door, the house of the *alpino* who was in Russia, and I knew that his mother was there; I shouted. But this woman was afraid and didn't want to open up. "I don't know anybody," she cried from the room above. They had had three *rastrellamenti* in the last few days at Frizzón, so this sense of reserve of hers was not unnatural, but I didn't realize why then and was very annoyed. "Let's hope that they'll open up to your son in Russia," I shouted at her, and then I was sorry. I went away to the house opposite, where Rosina and her father lived.

"There's nobody at home. They're all dead."

"Open up at once!"
"I'm dead too."
"Dead? What are you doing up there at the window?"
"I'm waiting for the hearse to take me away." *

But this was not how it was. Rosina and her father opened their door immediately. They were already up, out of bed, so I said: "What's the time?" It was past three o'clock, they said, in other words, past their time to get up. I was soaking wet; they made me strip naked in front of the fire and gave me some rags to put on. I told them what had happened to us, and they told me about these *rastrellamenti* in the village, and other things. They gave me a bowl of milk which I enjoyed very much; then I was sick and went to sleep. The father took me outside (the darkness was beginning to disappear) and made me climb into the loft, where there was no hay, so I lay down on the wooden floor with an army blanket over me; he took away the ladder, and must have said *buon riposo* too, but I didn't hear it, being asleep already; and then he was up again and trying to wake me up, which wasn't easy. He said the fourth *rastrellamento* had arrived, I had better leave. I said: "What time is it?" and he said: "Nine o'clock." I hoped at least he meant nine o'clock at night, but I realized it couldn't be that because of the sun outside. He made me go down by the ladder, then put me in the charge of a small boy who was waiting there.

We hurriedly crossed the street and descended into the heart of the valley directly below, until we reached a ledge that led to a cave. The rocks below were sheer. The boy left me, and as I sank into sleep again with the army blanket over me, I could hear the first shots at the entrance to the village.

I believe there were other *rastrellamenti*; for most of the time I slept, and every now and then Rosina came with

* Dialogue taken from *Pinocchio.*

170

milk and polenta, about once a day. I ate very willingly, and was at once sick, easily and effortlessly. We used to talk, too, before I went to sleep, and gradually I stopped being sick and we'd talk at greater length. This must have gone on for a week.

I had the impression of being under the protection of a village, but in reality Frizzón was not a village. As I have already said, there were five houses, and there were fifteen families in these five houses; the poverty was extreme and congenital. Still, they were people like us, they spoke the same dialect, their young men went off to the same wars, and they had the same religion, except that it was more inconvenient. There was a little church, a kind of private chapel, just above the five houses; but it was closed and I think they must have gone down to Enego for mass, weddings, and funerals—which would have taken quite a long time to get to, and much longer to come up from.

Rosina was twenty; she was the eldest of six brothers and sisters. The mother had died eight years before.

"She left five other children besides me, and the youngest was only five days old," Rosina said. She had thus to take on the job of mother when she was twelve.

"Christ," I said. "How did you manage, you and your father?"

"It's a hard life," said Rosina.

"What does your father do?"

"He's disabled, he looks after the animals."

"What do you eat?"

"Oh, things that grow around here," said Rosina. "And we drink milk." They had two cows.

It embarrassed me to drink these poor people's milk, even more to throw it up; but it was even more difficult to say no to it. I began to have the usual fantasies again, assuming they were fantasies, that the *popolani* were better than we were, infinitely better. In any case they were not just my own fantasies; I know that my companions shared them too. We, my companions and I, scarcely spoke about such matters in those months, but I was aware that they felt as I did and no less intensely. It usually came on us in a sort of flash, at different times and places, as chance would have it. Lelio's flash, for example, happened on the long march from the Bellunese to the Ortigara, when he and the others came up to meet us. They were very hungry and were certainly not in the mood to expatiate over the virtues of the mountain people. Yet one evening an elderly woman stood watching them as they approached her hovel; she was dressed in black, with a black kerchief around her hair, and looked at them without speaking. When they were in front of her, they stopped. Antonio asked her the way; at first she didn't reply (and Lelio wondered whether she might be one of those German-speaking creatures that inhabit some of the valleys in that area), but then she said in good dialect: "Would you like a plate of soup?"

This was the moment: because Lelio knew how little there could be to eat, and what it meant for her to offer it. And sure enough, when they followed her into the hut they found that the supper, cooking on the fire, was simply a soup of herbs, with some dry bread. There was an infant in arms waiting for its food, and a larger child seated at the table waiting for it too. Perhaps the woman was the mother, perhaps the grandmother. The soup they all shared, and the woman gave the dry bread to the men and the children.

These people, whether they were up on the mountains or down in the plain, had to cope with harshness in life all the time, and in comparison we felt like spoiled boys who insisted on having our civil wars, and got into trouble, and then had to go to them for help: and they helped us.

Almost all my companions went through something like that. With Gigi, for example, it happened in the plain much later on, when we went out to kill somebody and for a night were the guests of a widow, a peasant called Cinca. I don't remember Cinca any more, but Gigi had his flash then because he was a novice, and hadn't had the experience of being up in the mountains with us, so he took it all in and now he remembers everything about this Cinca, who he says was a paragon of a woman, and I readily believe it, except that I don't remember her.

I began to feel stronger, and Rosina even brought me a little *grappa*; * I believe they kept it as a sort of special treasure, to put it in coffee on feast days. She brought it to me in a glass bottle, the sort one puts medicine in, about half full; I took a sip, and when Rosina went away I took a couple more. As soon as the war's over, I'm going to buy them lots of *grappa*, I thought—but of course I never did.

I lay there in the dark, with this little bottle of *grappa* for company, and for the first time tried to think rationally about what could have happened to my companions during the *rastrellamenti*, and I hoped that perhaps some of them were still alive. I heard people coming along the path, giving the warning whistle and calling my name softly. A circle of flashlight appeared; it was Cris, with another. I had met him often, Cris, higher up in the Altipiano, but this was where he and his unit normally operated, on both sides of the valley. The other was the boy who had accompanied me to this cave the morning of my arrival.

"Do you feel like coming down to the bottom of the valley?" asked Cris.

He was tall, toothless, high-spirited: a bit of a daredevil.

"They've taken two of Maometto's boys," he said. "We're going to liberate them; we need someone who speaks German. You speak it, don't you?"

"I know how to say please and thank you," I said, "and words like Reason and Intellect; and my old grandmother roosts in the high tree."

"Could you pass as a German?"

"Of course not." To be shot as an impostor was bad

* Grape brandy.

enough, but to be caught making a shocking grammatical mistake . . .

"Do you know how to say, 'I have been wounded, open the door'?"

"Certainly I do."

"Let's go then," said Cris. "We've also brought you some *prugna.*" *

He too had brought it in a medicine bottle, the same size as the other, the color of barley sugar; it was full, and I (after tasting the brandy, which was excellent) put it in the crack which served as my cupboard, thinking: This is indeed an evening for medicine bottles, and I promised myself that I would give it to Rosina as a present. The one she had given me—also the color of barley sugar, though much lighter, and now a quarter full of *grappa*—I put in my pocket.

"I haven't got any shoes," I said.

Cris at once sent the boy up to the hamlet to find a pair; the boy had an elderly uncle, about my build; and this uncle had some shoes which he used when he had to go somewhere.

"And if we don't return tomorrow?" said the boy. "What if my uncle has to go somewhere?"

"Tell him he'll have to wait," said Cris, and the boy went away grumbling.

Cris explained the plan to me: it was a good one, though a bit dangerous. "You'll see it'll be good fun," said Cris.

"I haven't got a sten either," I said. "I left it in a hole."

"We can go and fetch it then. Is it far away?" he asked.

I felt a little pang of joy that what I had said had not horrified him.

"Two days to get there, and two to come back," I said.

Cris laughed and said: "Then I'll give you my P.38," and he took it out and gave it to me. I checked the magazine,

* Plum brandy.

the round in the breech, and the safety catch. It seemed like a dream: a P.38!

The boy arrived with the shoes. They were much too big for me. "He must have feet twice as large as mine," I said. The shoes seemed as if they were alive: inside they had regular lines of exposed nails like teeth, and as soon as a foot was inserted they bit it, though without really hurting.

"There are so many nails," I said. "Why doesn't your uncle knock them in?"

"My uncle is lazy," said the boy.

"Let's go," said Cris. And so we started to go down into the valley. It was the first time that I had done any walking for some days, but at that point of the Valsugana going downhill is not really walking. What with the darkness, and the *grappa*, and the *prugna*, and the incredible steepness of the descent, I seemed to take off at every step, as one does in dreams. I seemed to be doing nothing else except throw myself into small troughs of black air. Cris went first, or rather he was the first to throw himself into these black troughs, and I dived in after him without thinking. The boy came last. Cris slipped two or three times, and swore as if to explain that he had dived in by mistake; every time I fell on him, and after he had sworn he asked: "How do you say that in German?" But I didn't know how to translate these swear-words into German; however, I invented them so as not to give a bad impression.

As we descended, the proportions of the Valsugana seemed ever more monstrous; the drop is five thousand feet on one side, where we were, and perhaps four thousand on the other. I arrived at the bottom intact in body, but with my head whirling.

We stopped at a shrine, near an empty house. The Brenta was a few yards away. With Cris's flashlight I looked for a moment at the shrine, which was small and homely, and at the same time I shielded the light with my hand. I saw a picture of a woman, a light that had gone out, a bunch of wild flowers; underneath was written: TO SANTA BARBARA FROM THE MINEWORKERS. Nearly everybody has his own saint.

Two partisans arrived, the ones we had expected. They took us to a largish hut: inside a lighted candle, people asleep on the floor, a dismal feeling. I didn't look at anybody. The action was scheduled for the following day, toward evening. I threw myself on the ground between two sleepers, without even taking off the shoes with the nails. Before I went to sleep I spent a little time thinking about German participles and past tenses, and I must have gone on reciting things to myself while I was asleep, because in the morning when I woke up I spoke for a while in German without realizing it. *"Im Traum sah ich ein Männchen, klein und putzig,"* I said without opening my eyes; and the chap who had been sleeping next to me said: "What did you say you were dreaming about?" The point is that he said it in German. I had one of those starts that we call *tremoni* in our dialect. Hell, I thought, we've lost our way; I'm among Germans.

Cautiously I opened my right eye, and there sure enough was a German lying on the ground with his back to me; then I closed my right eye and opened the left, and there was another lying on his stomach. It was he who had spoken. I said to myself: My God, what now? Then I saw that he had his hands tied.

It was *they* who had lost their way. They had been captured two days before on the far side of the Grappa and had been transferred here; they were being held as hostages. They had already had their shoes taken off, but they still had socks on.

Outside the hut were two or three partisans loading tommy-gun magazines. They looked like excellent fellows. We were in shade, but a segment of sunshine was moving toward us, circumventing a buttress. Cris suddenly appeared in this sunlight; when he was near I smiled at him, and he returned the smile with his toothless mouth, and said: "The action is canceled. They hanged them an hour ago behind the village."

Then, after a little, he said to me: "Tonight we're going to take them down." And I said: "I'll come too."

Cris had a little bundle, in which there seemed to be some metal tools. We entered the hut together, and Cris said: "Ask them if they are real Germans." I asked them. They were real Germans; one was from a village near Bamberg, the other from the North. Cris said: "I'm hungry, what about you?" He took a large piece of fresh cheese out of his haversack and a cobbler's knife from his hip pocket; he cut two good pieces and gave me one. I helped it down with *grappa*. Cris said, with his mouth full, and looking at the Germans: "Ask them if they're hungry." I asked them this, and they said yes. Cris cut another piece and we fed it to them. His knife cut the cheese as though it were paper. "How it cuts!" I said. Blades have always fascinated me. "I've only just sharpened it," said Cris; he polished it on the palm of his hand, then leisurely tried out the blade on his nail, and put it back in his pocket.

The partisans were beginning to make preparations to leave, and it seemed that everyone already knew what to do. Perhaps orders had been given outside. I felt a bit stupid.

They gave the Germans back their shoes and untied their wrists so that they could put the shoes on; after that the wrists were tied again. Tie, untie, it was like a pantomime.

When it was evening we left, about four or five of us, with the two Germans in the middle, along a path skirting the bottom of the valley. In front was Cris with another, then a German, then me, then the other German, then the other partisan. Lastly came the boy from Frizzón. What he thought he was doing was not clear, but I think he followed us to keep an eye on his uncle's shoes.

After quite a while we turned right, across the bottom of the valley and toward the river, which we crossed cautiously by means of a small bridge with iron railings; then, following a lane among the fields (the valley was cultivated, about a mile wide), we went on as far as the railway escarpment, where the first houses of the village began.

We stopped near the main road. There was a wall there with an iron stake in it, and in front of the wall was quite a large shrine with a light burning in front of a big Christ stuck on the cross. The valley is full of shrines. The night was not completely dark, the moon was just coming up, and moreover there was the light of the lamp which reflected on the wall facing it. The two boys were hanging from this stake, back to back.

They looked extraordinarily like one another, and each had a placard hung around his neck, bearing the single handwritten word BANDIT: they were both without shoes. There was nobody about on the road.

"Were they related?" I whispered to the partisan next to me. He told me *sotto voce* which was the one called Rino, but didn't say anything about the other.

Behind the shrine there was a kind of little enclosed meadow, perhaps a disused cemetery, except that there were no gravestones or traces of graves. The iron gate was unlocked, and we went through it so as to be hidden from the road; we all sat down on the ground just inside the gateway, because the wall was not very high. The two Germans looked around anxiously. "Say we've got to leave them here, so we must gag them," said Cris. I told them this, and we tied our neck scarves around their faces. "Now tell them we're going to tie their legs too. Tell them we've got to leave them here for a little while." I told them this and they nodded yes with their heads. So we tied their legs too, and lay them on the ground leaning on their sides. Cris took out the cobbler's knife and kneeling behind one of these Germans, the one from Bamberg, put his left hand firmly on his forehead, as though to feel if he had fever, but rather more strongly; and with his right hand, with this knife, in

178

the circle of the light from the flashlight, he began to cut his throat.

I looked away and turned my eyes up to the mountain, already veiled in orange moonlight. I heard the noise of the Brenta across the fields, and a door banging in the village. I heard the German's legs pounding the ground, and I thought: Dying is a struggle, a lost battle.

We took the shoes off the Germans and gave them to the boy from Frizzón to hold. Then we dragged both of them out and pulled them toward the road until we had them beneath the two boys who had been hanged. They gave me the two placards on which BANDIT had been written, and I turned them over and wrote in large letters, with a blue pencil: GERMAN. This is my job, I thought, the literary part of the job. I had to spit on the pencil more than once, to make it write, because it was hard; the result was not very artistic, but readable. I was shaking a bit, because I had a high temperature: I could tell by touching my forehead.

In the circle of the flashlight I saw Cris's hands as he stuck the hooks in the slits in the throats, and again I looked away.

We left these butchered Germans there, with these placards, hanging from the stake; and we went away with Rino and his relative, if he was his relative. Cris carried Rino on his shoulders, and the second boy was carried in turns by two others. We passed near another shrine, of medium height; as I have said, there are masses of shrines in the valley. Under the arch, and I recognized San Luigi. Heck, I said to myself, I bet today is my name day.* Finally we arrived at an enclosed cemetery, more or less like the other, only that there were graves this time, also headstones. At this point I drank the last of the *grappa*, and looking at the bottle against the light, because there was a moon, I saw that the bottle was light; light barley sugar. The moon was orange. I threw the bottle against the wall and heard it shatter on a stone.

* San Luigi's day is June 21st.

"Quiet," said Cris, because we were near the road. The two dead boys were on the ground, side by side, and in the light of the moon I saw again how much they looked like one another. "Were they related?" I asked Cris; and he said no. I looked at the one who was not Rino, and said to Cris: "Did you know him?" And Cris said: "Yes."

The rest is confused. First we had to shovel earth out of a hole, then we had to fill the hole up again, and every now and then I took somebody's turn.

The partisans had begun to chatter among themselves, and I began chattering too, as I shoveled in the earth, but about what I don't remember. I believe they told me they wanted to go up the Grappa, and I told them I wanted to return to my cave up at Frizzón.

I was leaning against a stone, in front of the iron entrance; in my hand I had the P.38, and I thought: Now I must give it back to Cris.

The battle engulfed us in a single mouthful; I saw the shadows on the gateway, the black shapes of helmets, two yards from me; I fired the P.38. In a moment everyone was firing, both we and they, but we were all mixed up. A great black body fell literally on top of me, half recoiling among the stones; probably it had already been hit somewhere because it didn't even try to harm me. Instinctively I threw my arm around it; I looked for the place where the heart was and fired a shot. Now it will start bleeding, I thought.

Then the fighting had finished, there were people wandering around the graves, as though searching for one another. Then I was standing in front of a stone and reading the inscription by the light of a flashlight that I must have picked up from the ground: *"She rests in peace . . . from brief infirmity to eternal life . . ."* On the nearest grave there was someone lying face upward; he was wearing a helmet and was still alive, though just barely. Once more I calculated where his heart was and pointed the P.38, and fired. The P.38 just made a click; the magazine was empty.

This is the last distinct thing that I remember; but I do have an idea that there was a noise of vehicles arriving along the road, some confused shots, bursts of machine-gun fire, a march in the night; someone accompanying me—perhaps the boy from Frizzón—an interminable steep climb, and the moon which was orange and made me feel dizzy whenever I looked at it. All this happened in the black space of the Valsugana, a wound in my mind, during a night in June 1944, which I believe was the night of San Luigi. Cris disappeared in a *rastrellamento* in September and was never found; the boy from Frizzón grew up into a young man and died in Belgium, in a mine; of the others I know nothing, not even their names.

"You didn't even drink the milk yesterday," said Rosina. "I arranged for it to be brought to you because I had to go to Enego: and it's still where it was, untouched."

"I had a fever," I said.

"Something awful's happened in the Valsugana," she said. "Trucks were passing the whole morning. They'll come up here again as usual."

"No, I don't think so," I said. "This time they'll just concentrate on the valley."

"It's a good thing my cousin's back. He was down there yesterday."

"So was I," I said: carelessly, because I didn't mean to disclose what I'd done.

Rosina laughed and said: "Barefoot?"

I looked at my feet; it was true, they were bare.

"That's funny," I said, "where are the shoes?"

"You didn't have any," said Rosina. "Right from the beginning you didn't have any."

"I know, but yesterday I did have them."

"You had a fever, but no shoes."

It was true that I had had a fever, but I had had shoes too. I thought: The boy from Frizzón has completed his mission. So I told Rosina that two people had come, and we had gone down together on business, and they had lent me shoes.

"Obviously they've taken them away again," I said. "I was very sleepy, and I don't remember any more." After a little I said to her: "Look, they also left me a bottle of *prugna*, which I would like to give you, for you and your father." And I told her where I had put it.

I was sitting in front of the cave. She went in to fetch the bottle.

"This is the bottle I gave you," she said.

"No," I said. "It's a different one. Don't you see it's made of dark glass?"

"No," said Rosina. "It's made of clear glass."

I told her to try drinking my health with a sip of *prugna*, and she tried.

"It's not *prugna* at all," she said. "It's *grappa*."

"Yesterday it was *prugna*," I said.

"You had a fever."

Rosina went away and returned in the afternoon, in a state of agitation. "They've killed some Germans down in the valley," she said. "It seems they've hung them up on butcher's hooks." Then she felt my forehead and said I hadn't a fever any more, and I agreed with her. But ultimately war is all fever, a strange tertiary fever, with ropes and hooks, with feet at one moment in socks and at another in shoes.

8

WHEN I LEFT for the plain they dressed me half as a peasant and half as a skier, and Rosina brought me a pair of shoes that were too large. I recognized the shoes immediately, but said nothing; on putting my feet inside I found the same nails. I said good-by to Rosina, and she gave me a pie which she had made for me. So I left, climbing across the slope of the Lisser; I was limping, partly because I had hurt one of my legs and partly because of these nails. Every now and then I stopped to knock in these nails, using a stone as a hammer; but it was a hopeless job. I limped so much I had to have a stick; now that I was on the point of returning to the world of men and houses, I truly felt that I was dressed as a rebel, adorned as a rebel—almost colored and painted as a rebel. Naturally I had no papers or money, or even a handkerchief: only the dark blue trousers of a skier and the patched, colored, collarless shirt of a peasant. To blow my nose I took out a shirttail from my trousers and blew, because the other way of blowing your nose with the fingers, while satisfying aesthetically, is not practical. I don't remember ever having to blow my nose at all before, in the Altipiano; but now that I was going down I felt I was beginning to become civilized again, and I started to blow my nose.

I kept near the eastern ridge, along the length of the Brenta Canal; the slopes were very wide, smooth, and indescribably beautiful. I was just a speck walking in the emerald countryside, and I limped along happily.

When I reached the first villages, I walked around them, but I didn't bother about avoiding isolated houses and farms.

In one house, where I asked for water, they took me to see the grandfather of the family; he had been in bed in his room for a long while and spent his time spitting on a piece of yellow paper stuck on the wall opposite; every other day they changed the piece of paper. All the same, the grandfather followed the ways of the world with interest. "Are they winning, the black berets?" he demanded every now and then. They replied: "No, Grandfather, no," and he said: "Good, good," and rubbed his hands. This old campaigner filled me with a sort of gaiety.

I asked: "But, really, how is it all going, down in the plain? Are they winning?"

"Down there, no," the members of the family said to me. "And what about up where you've been?"

I said promptly: "Not even up there." And then I added: "They're only wasting our time, we keep on having to make fresh starts." "The whole lot needs to have its throats cut," they said, and I thought of replying: "I'll do my best," but instead all I said was: "Thanks a lot," and went away. During this exchange the grandfather spat three times.

I walked and walked, until I got fed up with being in the meadows, so I went down onto the main road where I walked more quickly, leaning on my stick.

Now I was conscious of that more luminous air which seems to circulate above the southern margin of the

184

Altipiano; it was as it is when one is approaching the sea and realizes from the color of the air that it's there, before one even sees it. The time must have been about five o'clock in the afternoon; when I heard the truck behind me, it was already too close for me to be able to slink away to the wood to safety. I continued walking, and as I did so made a quarter of a turn with my head, as though to look at a tuft of rhododendrons on the hillside. Out of the corner of my eye I saw the Germans. Two were in the cab, three or four were standing on the back with machine guns in their hands.

I wondered if they would shoot straight off. I was sure that they must detest skiers. The voice that called out to me was surprising. I turned and said to one of the two in the cab: "Oh, good morning, may I help you?" When uttering my first two or three phrases in a foreign language, I always tend to give an excellent impression.

"Would you like to come a bit of the way with us?" said the one who wasn't driving. "We're going to Conco and don't know the way. Can you show us?"

I didn't know either, but I said: "With much pleasure." This exchange of courtesies, pure peacetime stuff, was absurd. It was like being in a play, and I climbed into the cab. I spoke a little to the one who was not driving. He was a sergeant from Stuttgart, was thirty-five years old, and spoke to me about his family, about the bombing in Germany, and about his home town.

I put a hand over the lump that was the Canadian grenade in my trouser pocket, and began thinking up answers of every description—who I was, why I was there, why I was not a soldier, why I was dressed like this, and lame, and without papers. But the German from Stuttgart just spoke to me of Stuttgart. It so happens that the name of this town has always attracted me; so I entered into the spirit of the thing, and at the end I was almost sorry not to go on hearing more about Stuttgart. It was one of the strangest things that happened to me during the war.

At the crossroads, before coming to the ridge, I said: "I get out here, you go to the right. You'll be there in about two miles." It was not true, I didn't know the way to Conco, but I had to shake them off in time, those pacifically minded Germans.

The Germans turned down the road to Granezza. I suppose one could say that for me at that moment—with this strange comedy—our long June *rastrellamento* had come to an end. A few paces now, from the point where I stood, and I was on the tall southern ridge of the Altipiano.

Suddenly I saw the plain, the whole plain, as far as the Berici, the Euganian Hills, and the sea. I saw streams, roads, villages, that I recognized one by one in a kind of great lake; everything was enamel and gold; I could make out my own *paese*, in the distance to the right, under the hills which from where I was seemed quite tiny, and I felt a kind of emotion that I hadn't expected, as if I were a traveler in China arriving at the top of a remote valley and looking down to see below him the roofs of Thiene, the houses of Schio, and the hills above his own village, his own home.

I stood at the top of the great green slopes that slid away in beautiful, wide, limpid folds; the sun was low on my right, the shadows were longer than life-size; the light was bright and clean. I was standing up there on the ridge; the emotion passed, and I felt better. There was a long, long shadow under my feet. I saluted the villages of the plain.

While I was looking at the sloping meadows, the long shadows, and the distant plain, I heard shots behind me, not close but quite clear. They seemed out of place in such an idyllic setting, because the shepherds' huts here were inhabited, and there were animals about, and cowbells ringing, and shepherds standing at the doors of their huts, with bowls of milk in their hands. I went to chat with a shepherd, and he gave me some milk; at the beginning he said practically nothing, but then he began to trust me, perhaps because of the manifest honesty of my dialect—village dialect, not the impure dialect of the towns.

"There are three or four partisans up there, toward the Melette," he told me. "They arrived last night, perhaps it was they who were firing."

I decided to go back and look; it didn't seem likely to me that they were my companions, we were too far from the Colombara; but one never knew.

Within half an hour, as I was going up a valley at last light, I saw some people on a knoll near a wood, and as I approached I recognized one of them as a man named Suster. There was a woman with them too, obviously a messenger. They were pleased to see me, and I said: "Was it you firing?"

"Yes," said Suster. "There was a German truck."

"Two in the cab, and three or four behind?" I said.

"Yes," said Suster. "You saw them too?"

"I came up here with them," I said. "I only got out a little distance away."

"Then you were very lucky," said Suster.

The woman was a messenger who had just come up from the valley. She was a great big girl, in a blouse and trousers. She reminded me partly of a weight-lifter, partly of a heifer. She was called Gina.

"I thought it might be my friends firing," I said.

"Where did you say that you had had your *rastrellamento?*" asked Suster.

I really hadn't said anything, but apparently just to look at me was enough. "On the Colombara," I said. Suster said that in that case there was no telling where they might be. "I shall have to go down to the plain," I said. "They'll be in touch if they are alive."

We slept in the open, without a guard. There were five of us in all: four of them, and me. One had an infection in his foot, and they were thinking of staying there some days to wait until his infection had cleared.

187

"You shouldn't fire at trucks," I said, "when you've a bad foot."

"It was they who saw us," said Suster. "It was too late to hide."

Suster very kindly arranged for Gina to sleep between him and me. There was about two hundredweight of her. Every time my eye fell on the mounds of her flanks and the heroic acres of her thighs, I felt an air pocket in my blood. I was tempted to touch her, if only with the tip of my finger; but I absolutely didn't dare. She was lying with her stomach upward and before going to sleep she whistled a couple of tunes with considerable zest. "Go to sleep," Suster said to her, and she fell, I think, asleep. After a while she turned on her side, with her back to me. There were few stars in the sky; and between me and them was the huge black mountain of her bottom, on which I would have paid I don't know how much to put my hand.

If peace ever comes, I thought, I'm going to get myself a bottom like that, or an even larger one, and I shall bring it up here and have the satisfaction of saying: "This belongs to me." Then I thought: No, not larger. Just this size.

I began to feel sleepy; I was flying, and as I flew in my air pockets I slept.

Gina left the next morning; first she went to tidy herself up in the wood, with profound emotion on my part; and then, when she came back, we exchanged a few words.

"You're a student, aren't you?" she asked. I said that I was, and she wanted to know if I was at the technical school.

I said that I was at the University.

"Mother of God," said Gina.

"One doesn't learn anything there," I said.

After a while she asked me if I was studying to be a lawyer.

I shook my head, and she said: "What are you studying then?"

"Philosophy," I said. She asked what you did after you had

studied philosophy, and I said you took a degree. She wanted to know what you did when you had taken a degree.

"Nothing," I said. "You just keep it."

She asked me what you do for a profession, with a philosophy degree, and I said that you could teach, but usually those who knew philosophy did not teach it, while those who taught it did not know it.

"And what do the people who know it do?"

"They keep it in their minds," I said.

"And then?"

"And then, when they think, all that they think is philosophy."

"And then?"

"And then they die."

Gina listened to my replies with the air of someone who follows another line of thought.

"It must be nice to know it, this philosophy," she said.

"That's where you're wrong," I said. "It's not very nice."

Then she said good-by to us, and went off toward the clefts in the hills to our east, to return to the Valsugana. We remained there some hours without doing anything, and after a while I noticed that a storm was getting up.

High above us black clouds had formed around the mountaintop; below armfuls of mist were moving up the valley as though to bottle it up like corks. Everything was happening quickly; there was a marvelous sense of tension.

"There's another *rastrellamento* coming," said Suster.

"At this hour?" I said. It would have been just past noon, and *rastrellamenti* always began at dawn.

"Perhaps their watches are slow," said Suster.

We could see them distinctly in the valley, half a mile below us and approaching from where I had arrived the first evening. They were Italians. The storm was almost ready to break. The sky had become violet. There were the last dramatic preparations, with the clouds taking up positions, and the slopes of the mountain loading up with electricity. We felt this electricity accumulating in ourselves too; there was a tingling under our fingers where they touched the metal. I had taken the tommy gun belonging to the boy with the infection. We literally sparked; the tommy gun crackled between my hands. The people below began firing from two or three points and got ready to come up.

We couldn't move; behind us there was an area that was completely open, finishing on a steep, bare slope. "We'd better stay here," said Suster.

The blobs of the first rain splashed on our faces. In a moment we were in the midst of an electrified fog, stabbed through with lightning; the growing tension was almost hysterical, unbelievable. We fired a few odd shots, haphazardly. Then a sort of end of the world began: bursts of rain, hail, thunder. To our rear a parapet of turquoise lightning, short and continuous; in front single flashes, dancing, white. We saw the fog torn in two, and the dazzling forks leaping in mid-air. Suster and I were on our feet, turned toward the *rastrellatori*, but we couldn't see anything clearly any more.

I was fed up with *rastrellamenti*; fed to the teeth. But I felt exalted by the great noise, by the sense of being caught by irresistible forces. It occurred to me that it would perhaps be easy to end it all, to go down and meet them; in all this uproar I felt a languor, a sense of playfulness. "Let's go," I said to Suster.

We advanced against the *rastrellatori*, Suster, I, and one other, down the slope, in the midst of the lightning, and a rain such as one sees in films, with intervals of mountain hail; we were firing all the time. Halfway down I took out my Canadian grenade and entrusted it to the vortex of the rain. We descended the whole half mile without mishap; when we were at the bottom, there was nobody. Action suspended on account of bad weather. The storm had beaten them; weather permitting, they would easily have won another nine points for their sergeants' examination (part two, practical); three points awarded for each partisan liquidated.

It didn't thunder any more, it rained smoothly and finely and the air had cleared; we sneezed like men possessed. The barrels of the tommy guns were full of water; we tipped it out, then as we still had half a magazine each we fired it at the wood, laughing, and then went up again. The other boy was called Tecche-Tecche.

I believe that this curious excursion pleased Suster, and that he thought it was a proof of courage on my part. Instead of which it had been all due to the storm.

"Stay with us," said Suster while we dried ourselves; I felt tempted to do so, but resisted.

Suster told me I could be second in command; if I stayed with them, I would be a good influence.

"No," I said, "I don't want to command anybody. I want to find out about my friends, if any of them are still alive. It's best I should be with them, because then I wouldn't have to command or obey anybody; and above all I don't want to influence anybody. Of course among my companions I will sermonize a bit, because it's my nature, but then the others will sermonize too, so we'll be quits."

"What a long speech," said Suster, "just to say that you don't like it here with us."

"I like it too much," I said. "But one can't always indulge oneself."

I said: "See you soon" to Suster and went off, but I never saw him again, because in September he died, hanged at Bassano, and if I'd stayed with them I would probably have met the same end too, with supreme irritation because the thirty or so hangings at Bassano were done from a truck. The truck would stop by a tree, the rope—already tied around the prisoner's neck—was fixed to a branch, and the truck would drive away to the next tree. I used to find these beastly affectations of the Germans quite insupportable, even when they used ladders; and I'd have resented the truck very much indeed. Whenever I find myself in the street where the men were hanged, at Bassano, I pass on hurriedly; I feel I know which would have been my tree, and I prefer not to think of the other details. My tree is the one in front of the convent door.

So I said good-by to Suster, and left, weaponless; and in a couple of hours I was again above the southern slope of the Altipiano, like the other time, at the same point, at the same hour, with a long shadow under my feet, as if in between whiles I had just been dreaming. I looked down at the steaming plain beneath me and worked out my itinerary as if it were a relief map of the area, a thing that it has always amused me to do.

At that particular moment my companions happened to be about one hour away to my right in the Bosco Nero; I only had to be told. Needless to say, it's all there in Mazzini; because Mazzini is one of those people who knew everything in advance, like St. Augustine.

"The Captain must never give orders for an attack [he meant: or a retreat] *without having first indicated to his men, with the inevitable dispersal in view, the point of reunion when the engagement is over."*

If we had had this point of reunion, we would have been spared, after the engagement, a lot of fatigue, and I would have been spared several days of walking. My missing companions were in the Bosco Nero, and I never dreamed that they would be there; and in order to find them I had to go down to the plain.

This is how it was throughout the war: we had to discover everything on our own. It was a method that was slow and hard; the danger was that at the end of such discoveries the discoverers would be ended too. At any rate, after I had looked at my long, silly shadow on the emerald meadows, I went down.

The very day of our second *rastrellamento,* June 10th, Gualtiero and Giampa, friends of ours from the University, finished their preparations for coming up to us. They did in fact come, and I think that on their way they must have run into the *rastrellatori* on their way back. Both were tall, handsome fellows; one was fair-haired, eccentric, keen on sport; the other dark, bearded, lanky. They arrived just on the day that I was walking in my trance toward the northeast, while Dante was sleeping off his ghosts at Gallio; and they found the remains of our little band at Zebio.

"There's been a fair amount of moving about, you know," said Bene, to explain the situation. "Toni's gone, so has Nello, and Dante and Lelio." About me they said that they had found my shoes. "They were low-heeled shoes," said Bene, "because his boots had been burned a few evenings before. However, they're no use to us, his feet were too small."

"Where have they gone?" asked Giampa.

"*Mah*," said Bene, shrugging.

"The whole damned lot have kicked the bucket," said Enrico.

"That's cheering," said Giampa.

"Are there any weapons we can have?" asked Gualtiero.

There were, and they gave them some. "Magnificent," said Gualtiero.

It was like that: when one band disappeared another began to form at once. Our name, even when most of us had kicked the bucket, attracted new partisans. We already were part of their instruction.

Two or three of us were enough to constitute a band. It was the best thing about the whole business, we really did have a collective sense; two or three were not just half a band, but a band all right.

Mario, Enrico, Renzo, Dante: after the *rastrellamenti* at the beginning of June, these were for some weeks the pivots of the whole setup. Bene was there too, but not long afterward he sprained his ankle on a night march; and so rather than carrying him around on their backs, they put him in a cave, where they gave him some Germans and a few others to look after. But Bene was not a good warder, he tended to fraternize with everybody. In the prison-cave there were no guard duties, no timetable, no discipline: there was a kind of placid symbiosis of people seated on the ground. One of the prisoners even had a small revolver—goodness knows why it wasn't taken away when he was searched— and he showed it to Bene. "Take care you don't hurt yourself," Bene said. "They're dangerous toys, those things."

When Dante came to hear of this revolver during an inspection, he fairly hopped with rage. "You're utterly irresponsible," he said to Bene. "Reckless." Of course Bene's irresponsibility was a stylish thing, and very civilized. The revolver was confiscated.

The areas in which they operated were the Val Bella and the Bosco Nero, near Granezza. This is the southern section of the Altipiano—woodland, tourist country; attractive, but without the rugged beauty of the *massif* to the north. There are several quite good roads there, and supplies were easy to bring up, the villages being relatively close. There were several local boys about too, with some able leaders, including our old friends, the veterans from the Corno di Campo Bianco, Castagna and Finco, plus one or two new people, like Giuliano and Bigatto.

This was our brief heyday in June. Suddenly my friends felt themselves masters of a technique; they now knew how to handle their civil war. They even had a barracks in the wood; it had been constructed swiftly but solidly by the local inhabitants, and for some weeks they slept under a roof. Every other day there was some sort of Action; each was initiated by our companions, and all were rapid, simple, efficient affairs. I don't remember the actual order in which they happened: the pharmacist at Lusiana, the doctor at Rotzo, the pharmacist at Gallio . . . And at Cesuna? and Roana, Tresche-Conca, Camporovere? and Canove? and Conco? . . .

There were some cases where abduction was indicated,

and others that had to be dealt with on the spot. A few misunderstandings occurred, as when Enrico and Ferrabino went to Dr. Sterchele with the intention of dealing with his case in his own office. Enrico stayed in the waiting room; Ferrabino, who knew the doctor personally, went in at once. Enrico waited for the sound of the shot inside (there had only to be one), but instead there was none, and he began to get nervous because the Fascist barracks was very close. Finally he saw the door of the consulting room open and the doctor came out, small and vivacious-looking, and behind the doctor was Ferrabino, who was very tall.

"I have looked at your friend," said the doctor to Enrico. "As far as I can make out, there's nothing wrong with him." There had been a mistake: Ferrabino, seeing that this was not the Dr. Sterchele he knew, and being a responsible fellow, had not shot him but instead had allowed himself to be examined. However, they thought it wise to take the doctor away all the same. After all, by the laws of probability even this Dr. Sterchele might well have been a Fascist—I mean considering that most doctors were Fascists. Actually he wasn't; and therefore after a long march in his white coat, and after a courteous but exhaustive interrogation under the pines, they sent him back to his surgery to finish his consultations. It was to this very Dr. Sterchele that one night later on they took Ferrabino with a bullet in his buttock, and he very courteously took it out, a gesture from one friend to another.

The most usual type of action was the occupation of a village by night. They would set up roadblocks at the right spots, place a bren in front of the barracks, then a special patrol would go to the appropriate house (usually that of a doctor or pharmacist), accompanied by a local guide. Sometimes the person who was to be taken away did not want to open up; all he would do was peer out of a window. But that was not a very good idea. The noise of tommy guns firing suddenly among houses can be really terrific. The bren in front of the barracks let loose; the *signorine* flew.

If no one appeared at a window, the house would have to be broken into. Then my friends would withdraw from the village, following a planned itinerary—though occasionally there were delays. The guide would say, pointing at a house: "That belongs to Fascists," and Enrico would let loose with what was left in his magazine. Then the guide would say: "And that's one too," and Enrico would throw his last *signorine*.

On one of these expeditions, the most important road-block—that facing Asiago—had been entrusted to Bigatto and his men; he was a great Independent, in the same class as Finco, and famous for his prowess as a partisan and for his ferocity. When our friends heard them firing, they weren't worried because there was a bren at the roadblock, as well as half a dozen men, plus Bigatto, who counted as another half dozen. The roadblock was between a clump of trees, and it was there, when the action was over, that the whole unit repaired with the usual pharmacist in its midst. There was a silence among the trees, a strange silence; the bren was at its post, the barrel was warm, the cases of ammunition were lying all about the place; on the road, twenty yards farther away, toward Asiago, were two dead men in military uniform. Later Bigatto and his people were traced in the wood: terrified by their own shots, by the stupendous aria of the bren, they had run away, abandoning everything, weapons, the post, the enemy dead. Such a display of fear, such a show of panic, by the people's guard whose job it was to protect the Venetian intellectuals playing at banditry somewhat disturbed the Venetian intellectuals.

"Fools," said Dante. "You're utterly irresponsible."

"There was so much noise," said Bigatto.

It was the usual problem: whether to punish or not to punish. Enrico wanted a trial, at least, but Dante said: "Let them be." For there was still the trial of the Rotzo doctor ahead—or was it the Roana one? And now the trial of this new pharmacist. The administration of justice is always overburdened, in Italy, and always late. They were scrupulously honest trials, with witnesses partly obtained on the spot, and partly kidnaped for the purpose. Enrico always wanted to be the prosecutor; the defense for the most part was in the hands of Bene, and was conducted in a serious and intransigent manner, based on the analysis of facts though not neglecting points of procedure, and at certain moments involving anger and shouting.

"If you really believe that, then you ought to be put on trial too," shouted Enrico to the defense during the debate.

"This is a place for justice, not intimidation," shouted back Bene, waving his hand like somebody saying good-by, as he always does when he's angry.

One of these prisoners was not even given a trial. He was a doctor. When they had captured him he was in pajamas, so on leaving the house they had wrapped him up in a blanket, because the night was cold, and he kept this blanket around him all the time.

"Who is going to take charge of the trial?" asked Bene.

"I say that we shouldn't try him," said Giuliano.

"Are you mad?" said Bene. "Do you want to slaughter him like a dog?"

"I say send him back home," said Giuliano.

"What *do* you mean?" asked Enrico.

"We're getting rid of too many doctors," said Giuliano.

"They should stick to being doctors," said Enrico, "and not be Fascists."

"I don't think this one is quite such a shit," said Giuliano.

"What *do* you mean?" asked Enrico.

They said that perhaps there had been a mistake; this doctor, yes he was a Fascist, but in fact he was not the worst sort of Fascist. There was not a clear case for bumping him off.

"This is irresponsible," said Dante.

"We've got to be fair to the prisoner," said Bene. "If the

judicial inquiry is suspended, then we've got to apologize to him."

"Naturally he's still a bloody old Fascist, whatever we do to him," said Giuliano.

"We could bite off his ears," said Bigatto, who was one of those who had this fixation.

"If you touch him I'll resign," said Bene.

"From what?" asked Enrico, which took Bene aback.

"If you touch him we'll put *you* up for trial," said Dante, and Bigatto went away grumbling. Since the incident with the bren he had lost all authority. The prisoner, after being duly warned, was set free, wrapped in his blanket.

As I walked down the slope (it was long, easy, without cover, and led into the vineyards and the cultivated fields above the first villages of the plain), I thought again of Suster, and of his invitation to stay with him. We spend our time looking for Italians, I thought, and when we find a good one we go away.

After I had gone down about half a mile, it was too late to repent; what is done is done, I said to myself. And so I left the mountains.

At first dark I was down, at Fara. Here I knew that there lived a peasant of my acquaintance, one who'd been in the *alpini*, so I asked to be directed to his house. He and his family made a great fuss over me. No one mentioned the word "partisan," but their admiration was obvious, and I was made to eat as much as I could. This was just as well, because I was still half a province away from my destination, and theirs was the last house I could safely enter. They look on us as their armed forces, I thought. It's a shame that sometimes they find us in this rather disarmed state. They gave me a supply of bread, and my peasant-*alpino* friend took me to the bank of the Astico and said good-by to me, and off I went, along the riverbank.

I knew that I must follow the Astico at least as far as

Sandrigo. By night one gets confused, but I had it all worked out: when I came to the first bridge, that would be Sandrigo, and there I would have to leave the river and walk across the plain in an oblique line; before night ended I would have crossed all the big roads, which were the most dangerous obstacles; then I could make straight for the hills, and climb up them even in daylight.

At midnight, when I reached the bridge at Sandrigo, I suddenly began to feel sleepy, and said to myself: Now I'm going to rest for ten minutes. I lay on the bank face upward. The water flowed in the Astico, there were masses of stars, the air was fresh and pleasant; so I closed my eyes for ten minutes, at midnight, and woke when the sun was high. I thought that with a bit of luck I could walk by day too; indeed, I was almost pleased that I had to do it that way as I had begun to realize the disadvantages of going across the plain by night, especially on account of the irritability of certain dogs.

I walked all day through the fields, avoiding villages and houses, and anything that seemed too human; I felt as though I were in occupied territory. The grain in the fields was ripe: I seemed to have skipped a whole season, or to have been transported into another country with a different cycle of seasons; here it was already full summer, and suddenly I felt the full force of the earth and the sun.

I stopped, to eat the last piece of bread that I had been given, and sat down on the edge of a field of wheat. I looked at the seams of scarlet poppies, and the blue clouds of cornflowers scattered about in the young gold. I sat on the edge of a ditch, my eyes about the height of the ears of wheat. Now that I was closer I could see that most of the ears were still not quite ripe; there was a suspicion of greenness that was gradually disappearing, drying out in the sun; but many others were perfect: a dry gold. I stared at these little sheafs mounted on gold stems; I felt overwhelmed with the thought of the plain making this grain, and of its having done so for thousands of years, and that we eat it.

How ancient it is, I said to myself: how perfect. I stood there, thin, imperfect, recent, with this piece of bread in my hand, and thought: What a strange beast man is.

I crossed the main roads with special caution. The dream geography of childhood became real; I had it right under my feet. As soon as I had walked quickly across our road, the one that links Vicenza with my village, near the church at La Motta, I knew that the river *must* be just beyond, because you can see it go in that direction at Castelnovo, where the road leaves it, only to rejoin it after La Motta; by then the river has changed its name, but you know that it's the same one.

And so in fact, just a few score feet from the road, there it was. It was completely dry, narrow, a bed of dry stones between the high banks; it was like a toy. As a child I used to think of what a marvelous adventure it would be to follow it up or down stream, for miles and miles, through unknown country, away from the familiar world of roads. I thought of it as being narrow, mysterious, encased between the banks; now I had found it and it was just that. The temptation even came over me to let everything go bust and to start following its course now; after all I was free, almost as if on holiday.

But instead I crossed it, and made for the hills ahead, knowing that at the second little parallel range I would find the hamlet and the house I was searching for. I was glad to have walked by day rather than by night among the dogs, many of which at that time were being left off the chain and thus were a constant nuisance.

The hillside was densely covered with cultivated farmland and chestnut trees; there were also tracts of quite thick scrub, in June leaf. On the top of the hill I took a footpath that led toward a house; here began one of the major dangers of my war.

On the footpath, between the thick hedges, under the shadowy branches, there was coming toward me a creature which had seen me but was not looking at me. It was nearly the same height as I and, being indisputably a dog, a very alarming sight. I had never seen a dog like that, and have never seen one since. It was a monster; its color was black. I am not afraid of dogs, provided I have something at hand to deal with them. Once, when we were cadets at Merano, Lelio and I had gone to an orchard to steal apples, because we were hungry, even though the apples were ugly-looking and sour. A German woman, also rather ugly, came from the house with two Alsatians, which she was holding by their leashes. She incited them, shouting in German. We began to go away, but the German woman continued to follow us with her dogs. All at once I thought I might as well turn around, and so I did. With a theatrical gesture I unsheathed my bayonet. The dogs, silly idiots, went on barking as before, but the German immediately changed her tune and, in terror, tried to drag them back. Then I began to grind my teeth and made a face as though I were going to kill all three. Now the German was shrieking in Italian "No, no," and made a wonderful spectacle of herself with her perfectly useless dogs.

"You ugly, diseased whore, you," I yelled at her. "Don't you understand I'm hungry? You revolt me, you and your dogs." So I filled my jacket with sour apples, under her eyes, then I filled my *alpino* hat too, and went up to Lelio and gave him some.

I can therefore claim that I am not really afraid of dogs, if I have something suitable in my hand; but otherwise I *am* a little afraid.

The hound of the Apocalypse came on without looking at me, and I continued toward it, slowing down a little but pretending to keep up the same rhythm of pace, because in such cases if you change your rhythm you provoke a crisis; but I have to admit that my knees were shaking. So we met. I kept my head up and watched it out of the corner of my eye, desperately searching my mind for something out of Jack London about fighting with dogs—though with little real hope. We passed, almost grazing one another, and I heard him growling to himself; he was still looking away, and I kept my eyes on him but with my head facing the front as before. When we had passed I again looked straight ahead, and deliberately didn't turn again; I know nothing more about this gigantic dog, and I've never since seen another approaching its size.

9

OUR LITTLE WAR had reached home territory, it had become civilized. Now we were up among our own hills, behind Isola Vicentina; it was like a cradle, a cradle of friendly mountains, covered with tufts of chestnuts, acacias, hazels, and brambles.

The plain was just a step away: as we sat on the dry stone walls, our feet seemed to dangle over the orchards of Isola; one could drop a pebble, almost spit on the road where the Fascist columns and ugly snouts of the German vehicles passed. The Germans had established themselves in all the principal towns of the plain; the Ukrainians were installed at Marano; the Fascists were at San Vito. We were cheek by jowl, on top of one another, in this area so crowded with towns, villages, hamlets, farms.

In the piazza at Isola there was a placard which said in German: *Area of Bandits.* This meant us. In all the towns there were bilingual notices saying how many pounds of salt each one of us was worth. People, however, didn't want this salt and said the Germans could shove it up, specifying exactly where. Within five minutes from Isola (sharp turn in the piazza, cross the bridge, change gear) the Germans could come straight to where we were encamped, a few hundred feet above the plain. The roads were uncomfortable but practicable; we didn't even have sentries. Yet the Germans still tried to take us with salt.

We didn't have sentries because there wasn't any need; the people stood guard for us—the peasants, the population in general. We were so mixed up with them, among the crops and plowed fields, the scrub and terraced hills, that we didn't even have to employ messengers, the news reached us by word of mouth. The farmers and peasants, however prosperous or poor, were our friends; for them life continued more or less as always. It was a regular scheme of things that had been going on for centuries, except that there had been a war in these past years—and now, in these recent months, there had been all these partisan boys about the place. The women often cooked something for us, the families received us freely into their homes, and on Sundays they would send us a bottle of wine.

Indeed, on our arrival we found them brewing *grappa*, illegally of course. We arrived singly or in pairs, one afternoon at the beginning of July, part already armed, part unarmed, some from the hills on foot, some through fields of sorghum, some on bicycles along the road and with false identity cards. Arrangements and appointments had been made, orders sent out, mostly by means of girl-friends, friends of girl-friends, and girl-friends of friends; everything worked smoothly. After those months of running wild in the mountains, there was something companionable and domestic about it all. I was one of the ones who came through the sorghum; I emerged finally on a threshing floor at the foot of the hills. They were all there. There were the survivors from the Altipiano, Dante, Mario, Enrico, Bene; there were other friends from our Vicenza group, Marietto, Gigi, and some new ones; and there were the peasants who made the *grappa*. It seemed like a country *festa*. The cordiality of it all immediately went to my head; here we were, down at the bottom at last, partisans among real men and women, rebels with roots. I was hot and thirsty; a peasant smilingly offered me a bowl three quarters full of limpid *grappa*, colorless like fresh water. I took it in my two hands and drank it without drawing breath. It was at that last grade at which one can barely distinguish *grappa* from pure alcohol. Everyone laughed, and I said: "Here's to the war."

For a quarter of an hour I behaved more or less as before; then things began to change. The afternoon became incredibly intensified and shone like fire; then it quickly began to fade, and went out. First noises disappeared, then colors, then the *Dasein* of things, then the *Sein* of the *Dasein*. At the end I even lost the sense of words, first the adjectives and the nouns, then those wretched verbs, and gradually all the rest; some pronouns remained and some ejaculations, which tended to turn into one another, like objects which change color. Finally there remained only the I and the non-I, and soon one of us left too.

We seemed to be on a busy frontier; before us the Germans and Fascists, to our rear partisans of every hue. Civilian life continued on its own account; so did the European war (though farther off). Our own war was based on a complex of relationships: of the plain with the hills, the villages with the fields, the *comitati* with the bands, the bands with the bands. The territorials, the population, the fiancées, even the enemy created a complex network of exchanges and traffic.

When we had left to go up into the mountains, it seemed that the popular resistance in the plain had finished, and that it was up to us to take the honor of Italy into our charge, and to watch over it jealously. Later, when we were forced to descend to the plain again, we foresaw nothing good. But we might have spared ourselves these anxieties: Italy in our absence had behaved very well.

The population of the Alto Vicentino was all on our side. The hills, the fields were full of partisans: all sorts of organizations had formed everywhere; with the good weather the popular movement of the previous autumn had increased in vigor, in more specific and tenacious forms. We were not alone any more, indeed we felt we had given too much importance to our solitude. Now there were units, zones, sectors, commands; there were branches, military grades of rank, liaison units, dispatch riders, badges, pass-words—and weapons too; it was a world complicated and chaotic, but real. We had a great hunger for reality, after those hallucinatory months in the desert. Now all that was needed was for us to take our place among the others.

We went at once to take it, our place, above the houses of Isola; from there we could see a great section of plain, toward Thiene and Bassano and toward Schio and the mountains. We were on the horn of a little bay, with the hump to the west. The diameter of this bay was a mile and a half, the height of the hills nine to twelve hundred feet; below one of the horns there was Isola, below the other Santomio. High on the crest there were two little villages, permanently in the hands of partisans, called Torreselle and Monte Pulgo. Fate had brought us here, very close to my home, to territories where as a child I had already played at war with my friends.

It was full summer; we were all mixed up with the cultivated fields, the dense bushes; one always had the feeling of emerging from branches or furrows. There were wagons, animals, hay, agricultural implements, farm equipment; we were ruddy-cheeked, befeathered with ears of corn. We drank with the peasants, laughed with their women, sang on the threshing floors. The summer brought forth fruits and flowers, and among the festoons were our faces suffused

206

with health. The hedges, the brush, the coppices stood host to our nests like cocoons stuck between the branches; I even had a little camouflaged tent among the acacias.

In the full bloom of that summer I felt healthy and strong as never before or after. I was almost fat; I felt physical strength welling up inside me. I felt so strong that, when I wrestled with my companions and put my arms around them, I had to be careful not to crack their bones. We wrestled, panting and laughing. We were all very strong, and our holds were formidable.

Girls came looking for us, in their summer frocks; sweethearts, school friends, and just friends. They dressed as for a holiday, and it was a pleasure to receive them, to make a circle seated on the grass and to chatter away among their light, bell-like skirts. Simonetta came to see Enrico. She was dressed in blue. I didn't have a girl; I was sitting in front of the tent and dismantling my pistol, which was just a dreary old Italian one, though caliber nine. Simonetta appeared under the shadowy branches and said: "Hello, doing anything nice?" I said: "I'm dismantling this. Then I'm going to reassemble it." I felt a little embarrassed. Simonetta was pretty and self-possessed, she read the hermetic poets, did rock-climbing, rode a motorcycle, and dressed elegantly. I think that at that time she was already preparing for her degree in engineering.

She stood watching me for a while; I really didn't know what to say, especially as she was Enrico's girl. Then I said: "Do you know about the caliber nine Beretta?" and she said no. "Would you like me to explain it to you?" I asked. I spent a delicious half hour, under the tent, explaining. It was simple comradeship, but very agreeable. However, my sex had swollen, it seemed bulkier than the pistol and much too bulky for the narrow tight khaki trousers that I was wearing at that time.

"Simonetta," I said.

"Eh?" she answered.

207

"Have you ever fired a pistol?"

She laughed and said no, and I said: "I'd like to teach you." Simonetta said: "I'd like that too." She was good at everything, and I was sure that she would have fired it very gracefully.

We were silent for a while, then I said: "Let's go and see where the others are." They were under a row of vines, the girls gathering up empty glasses and tablecloths from the grass and preparing to go away. The partisans, more or less in uniform, watched them with friendly eyes. It seemed the nicest moment of the war.

I had come down from the Altipiano to get news of the others; I took it for granted that later we would go up there again, that our place would be in the high mountains. When I was down, I changed my mind. Up there was too easy, I said to myself; we must wage war right in God's own country, not in the Thebaid. We must try to do a little terrorism—make it concrete and daily, organize ourselves so that we won't just be meat for a *rastrellamento*. We must stay down here and make ourselves the strongest of the lot; we've had enough of the luxury of being weak, alone, virtuous, *rastrellabili*, exterminable.

I don't know whether I ever got around to sending a message about these things to my friends, when I found out where they were, or whether they came to the same conclusions on their own. The fact is that in July they came down too, in a couple of nights, on foot and armed, proudly crossing through darkened villages, like veterans who disdained to go around them for safety's sake.

Renzo had not come. He stayed up there, in circumstances that have never been made really clear. Some news about him began to reach us: that he was alive and attached to some local Communist units on the western edge of the Altipiano, or perhaps these units were attached to him. He was known as Tempesta, and spent the rest of the war apart from us, with this name; he grew mustaches (so we were told) and these became large and twisted, really tempestuous, the color of copper; he already had a terrible reputation, and this in the nine remaining months of the war steadily grew. From the timid little rebel that I remembered on his arrival at the Altipiano—slender, reserved, all absorbed by his own silent and inexplicable problems—there emerged this great brute, almost as hard as the landscape up at Rotzo, except that he had (which the landscape of course lacked) that special venom that comes from a cultivation of the intellect.

Giampa and Gualtiero stayed up there too, and subsequently with the partisan brigade known as the *Sette Comuni*; all three of them wintered in the mountains, emissaries of Vicentine civilization in that long, last, barbarous winter of the war. Their fabulous adventures do not form part of this story; but we counted their glory as our own. After the liberation, when they appeared, hairy, terrifying, picturesque, on the streets of Vicenza, they were so perfect that people felt inclined to say: "Go back, and always stay like that."

Why they didn't come down with the others to the plain is not clear. For Giampa and Gualtiero it was probably too soon, seeing that they had only just arrived; for Renzo perhaps there had been some question of a disagreement, a tiny bit of impatience with aspects of both his and our ideologies, or perhaps it was just an impulse. Our friends only gave vague explanations.

"Why isn't Renzo here?"

"Well, you see, he'd gone up to Campo-gallina," they said.

"What do you mean?" I asked. "Why didn't you wait for him?" and they replied: "We gave him the slip." This didn't seem very amusing to me at the time, but looking back it has an authentic and typical ring. One did many things on an impulse—without caring about the consequences. I can now imagine what happened. Renzo coming back from

Campo-gallina, weary and with a heavily loaded pack, to find only locals from Asiago.

"Where are the *tusi*, the boys?"

"They've gone down to the plain; they said that they were going to do some concrete terrorism."

"And when will they return?"

"Who knows?"

"And what message did they leave for me?"

"None."

"Shits," said Renzo; and in his fury he at once went off in search of Communists. On finding some on the western ridge he joined up with them, and began his career as Tempesta. Soon his terrible red mustaches started to sprout, and all through the autumn and winter they prospered.

There were again a dozen of us, nine permanent and two or three attached in a desultory way, all armed with sten guns, except Raffaele, who had come with a machine gun, and Marietto, who had the old 91. We put Marietto last, with his 91 over his shoulder, when we went in single file. The tall barrel looked like an antenna. Marietto was short-sighted, new to military service, and when he carried his gun his face would flush with pleasure. He was the youngest of us, a first-year student of philosophy, very bright. The squad was perfect, I thought, as we filed along the path. There was more grammar among us, more syntax, more eloquence, more dialectic, more science pure and applied than in any other partisan squad since the time of the Maccabees. If one could wage war with examination marks the Germans would have had a bad time of it. Instead we were rather embarrassed by our prowess as students, especially with the newcomers, Raffaele and Severino, who were from different backgrounds.

It was a real relief to have a man like Severino among us. We spoke of Gentile's "pure act"; he spoke of things that were palpably impure. We explained to him about the

Girondins and the Jacobins, and how they operated, and he told us about his friend who had piles and no money to have the operation done, and who thus had to perform it on his own. This friend tied himself to a beam in his bedroom head down in front of the wardrobe mirror, and with a cutthroat razor he operated on himself. The blood fell into a bowl placed on the ground. Severino's friend did practically everything with ropes, even when he made love to his wife.

"Couldn't we recruit him?" we asked; he sounded like an interesting acquisition. But Severino had lost touch with him and said: "Perhaps he has joined the Black Brigade."

Raffaele too was a novelty to us. He was our age, but seemed younger; he was a handsome, soft-spoken, fair-haired young man, and arrived with a machine gun. He had the appearance of somebody who had run away from home, who had literally just interrupted a game with his brothers. Instead he knew all about danger and violence, more than we did. In peacetime he was a daring rock-climber; earlier in the war he had been with a special antipartisan unit in Croatia. He and this unit used to go into the woods there, not to fight partisans, but to exterminate them, just like that. They went about these woods as though they too were partisans, and when they found a group of real ones, partisans, seated in a circle around a fire, they crept up very slowly and exterminated them. Sometimes of course it was the real partisans who themselves did the exterminating; but at any rate Raffaele stayed alive, and at the armistice he had kept his machine gun and now he was with us. I looked at the machine gun that had done the exterminating and thought: How complex are the operations of history.

Our semiofficial leader was Dante; we had re-elected him informally. He was reluctant to accept the post, but we had been firm, we had *ordered* him to command us. In reality our commander was a kind of chairman; all main decisions had to be taken democratically, even in the presence of the enemy. We put almost everything to the vote, even—if need be—in whispers. It happened that we each found ourselves being vice-commanders in turn, usually when something cropped up that one of us might be particularly keen about. I think I did more vice-commanding than anybody else, at least in practice; it's true that I considered myself equal in rank with the others, but it's also true that I gave a great many orders.

Now we no longer felt like apprentices, but masters in our own right; jealously independent, disciplined, polished. The Communists did the most shooting, and caused the most damage, in a somewhat heavy-handed way, but we had a more lively sense of the consequences of shooting and causing damage. We did nothing that was not impeccable from the standpoint of what we tended to call ethical-political fairness. There were times when we seemed to fire too little and not cause enough damage; we were inclined to accuse ourselves of inefficiency, but now it is clear to me that our scrupulousness was not without value and that we were not in fact *worse* than the Communists. They had commanders and commissars already wedded to a general doctrine about man, and society, and the war in general, and so on; they had behind them the whole setup of international Communism, which is certainly one of the most impressive setups in the world (but of course it was not they who'd invented it). We didn't have anything: we had to justify every modest explosion, the smallest death.

We liked our work to have finesse, to be well planned: we were almost ceremonious when we shot at the windows of collaborators; sabotages had to be nicely synchronized, kidnapings civilized, executions scrupulous. Harsh and severe in our conceptions, we were polite and almost gentle when it came to the deeds themselves. It didn't even enter our heads to shoot someone out of hand. What was more, we didn't want to blow things up without paying for them (by vouchers), nor yet to frighten people needlessly. We didn't like to go through with an assassination without an explanation first, preferably to the victim concerned; if we couldn't do that, it would be to one another, either before or after the event. These were our intentions: in practice we didn't blow things up much, we only caused moderate alarm, we hardly assassinated anybody at all. As with the great chess players, by far the most important moves were those that were never made. But it mustn't ever be said that we were lagging behind. Our job no longer had any secrets for us; we felt like a group of artisan-artists with a severely limited production and a subtle technique, and with a strong sense of professional and personal autonomy.

I believe that we were the only ones in the whole area, right up to the end, to do without cover-names. Their usefulness seemed doubtful to us, their style repugnant. This arcadia of names is an old Italian malady, I thought. So I proposed, and it was agreed, that in the midst of all these fellows called Tiger or Hawk or Thunderbolt we should remain Mario, Severino, Bruno. Bruno was one of our Vicenza boys, but he wasn't with us throughout the whole period; when the Communists came to see us, he used to put a long white feather in his black hair and received them thus. While Russians and Allies were twisting the neck of Nazism, we felt we must at least do the same to rhetoric.

Perhaps the most important thing was to be there at all; to let ourselves be seen armed on the top of the long crest which runs along the main road, all the way to Vicenza. We often went along it, the crest, from Torreselle to Ignago and then to Monteviale. Down below, the plain belonged to the enemy—at least by day it did; up here a stone's throw away, the little kingdom of the hills belonged to us. There were conventions just like those separating states. Certain things were tolerated. We could go down at our own risk, and in fact we did go down; they could come up to *rastrellare* a little and in fact sometimes they did do so. But just as we didn't presume to occupy their territory, so they didn't seriously presume to occupy ours.

We exercised this precarious, adventurous dominion over

the little villages in the hills; at night we descended to do our work in the dark countryside. We had new plastic explosives, which a technical expert had come up from Vicenza with a suitcase to explain to us. He had arrived on a bicycle, with his fake identity papers and impersonating a traveling salesman who dealt in vests and pants. The detonators were little tubes of thin copper, painted in bright colors, blue, red, or violet; inside there was a phial of acid which one broke by biting the copper covering with one's teeth. The color indicated different timings, but sometimes I liked to imagine that they would result in blue explosions or violet ones, or—at daybreak—orange.

Dawn at the camp would find us with our faces turned east, eyes straining to catch the flashes of explosions deep in the bosom of the night. Weapons, British shirts, detonators, and margarine reached us by night too. I made up the passwords for the parachute drops, but had to abandon the best ones that occurred to me. The announcers on Radio London would rather have gone on strike than let themselves say such things out loud.

The drops in the plain were something to be remembered. Pitch dark, because they chose the nights without moon; "blind" meetings, masses of people flocking in from every corner of the horizon, and whispering as they gathered in the depths of the countryside. When we heard the rumbling of the plane, we lit fagots to mark the meadow; a flashlight signaled in Morse: *It is here, drop.* Soon the black sky was filled with the phantoms of great parachutes arriving; we hurriedly divided up the material without knowing what was there, and started to carry it away. The dogs barked for miles around.

I found myself alone with Marietto in the middle of the fields, with the wrong load as usual, staggering among the uneven furrows. He was shortsighted even in daylight, and at once went slap into a row of vines; he fell in a most impressive way. To carry a hundredweight is nothing, the tricky thing is to get it on one's shoulders. We spent the night trying to do this. I wondered whether appropriate legends came into his mind: Atlas, Hercules, Sisyphus—there was something of all these in our civil war, in the whole experience, but mainly it was Sisyphus. What we did kept being undone. What we carried up the mountain rolled down again; it seemed a never-ending process. Crawling and rolling, Marietto and I arrived at the camp just as dawn was approaching.

We particularly noticed the abundance and varieties of forms going on around us—the dense intermingling of partisan life in summer, the vitality of Italy.

In the villages there were the territorials, ensconced in their own houses, either virtually in hiding or—more often —exempted in some sort of way from military service. They kept their weapons hidden in orchards or attics; they used to turn up at some of the night meetings, usually just so that they could be counted, receive orders, and go and get stuff that had been dropped by parachute. They were in fact the direct heirs to the people who in every village, right from early on, wanted to hold themselves in readiness for the "opportune moment." They represented the moderate, opportunist, wait-and-see wing of the Resistance. But now we realized their importance to us. It was they who organized the rations and supplies, who liaised with the *comitati*, warned us of impending *rastrellamenti*, supplied news, suggested specific actions.

The military commands in the plain were primarily concerned with these useful shadows, and thus often gave the impression of being too cautious and moderate. In actual fact there were some excellent fellows among the leaders down there, like our bearded Count at Santomio, and the dynamic youths who ruled the line of villages on our eastern horizon, from Dueville to Thiene and to the Val d'Astico.

These were bent on waging war seriously, and worked in the plain to extract new nuclei for mountain formations out of the territorial conscripts; their job was more dangerous than ours, and one could not say that they didn't pay for it personally. Of those that we knew best, one was hanged, one deported, and two were killed in armed exchanges. Our Count, taken in September by the ugly bastards of San Vito, and interrogated mainly up his bottom, and in other charming ways, succeeded in converting one of his jailers during the intervals of being interrogated, and escaped with him; and strangely it was the jailer, in the guise of a partisan, who was eventually killed by the Fascists.

But, on the other hand, some of the other territorial leaders, especially those at local level, seemed to be real go-slowers by vocation, true extremists of moderation. For them it appeared that the bands on the hills were a sort of inevitable evil; and they treated the impatience to "do something," felt by many of their boys, as a disturbing element that was simply plain tiresome.

There were about half a dozen in my brother Bruno's squad, two workmen, two peasants, one landowner, one student. They had no "papers," and didn't want any; they wanted tommy guns, and to be free to roam about. The members of the *comitato*, loyal to the local leader, ordered them to give up their weapons; this was at a farm, on the threshing floor. For a while they negotiated, then Bruno's boys surrounded the whole *comitato*, slipping back the safety catches of their tommy guns. Then the *comitato* gave them permission to carry on.

They remained out all summer, as an autonomous unit. A fair-haired peasant was in command, a survivor of one of the bloodiest encounters on the Pasubio. They went around the villages, through orchards and gardens; they worked their way through the hamlets and villages of the plain, right up to the foot of the hills where we were. They had the warm support of the young peasant girls, who laughingly offered them the liberty of the big farmhouses, and all their resources. They even gave themselves a uniform—short trousers and linen shirts, all the same color, sky-blue; they seemed more like a sports team than a military unit, and were as proud of their weapons as if they were nice new bicycles. The desire for glory in battle (which sometimes flickered through our minds) didn't matter in the slightest bit to them, but if the occasion arose they were perfectly content to open fire; and their presence out there in the fields of the plain meant that in practice even that territory was more ours than the others'. During the big *rastrellamenti* they would be up in the hills in a couple of shakes. Once during a long *rastrellamento* by the Ukrainians Bruno and his companions came up as our guests for a few days. What struck them most was the austerity of our diet; because we still mostly ate polenta, with margarine from the parachute drops. Our guests, used to the abundance of the countryside, to things like chicken and watermelon, looked with amazement—not unmixed with compassion—at this collection of savages, which we were, among the bare fields of the hills, with our Spartan meals; and during that brief period they imposed a regimen of good living upon us.

The hills were full of mountain partisans, forming more or less regular units, complete with squads, camps, and a certain amount of discipline. They were based on local recruiting and tended to operate near their own *paesi*—now in German hands. They were called bands, and were quite numerous, and excellently commanded by leaders such as Tar, Tigre, and Negro; theoretically they were part of larger formations such as brigades and the like, but in reality they were autonomous. Their method of waging war was rapid and brisk; they were continually active, out on expeditions, capturing people, having little firing matches with the enemy. Tar, the prince of the mountains to our rear, was the man with a fur cap whom I had known during the first secret meetings in my *paese*. Now he was the legendary head of a band, and had changed his headgear. He wore a colonial helmet. His kingdom was large, centered on the knot of hills behind the village, branching up along the ridges which go toward Schio, and down to the south along the forked ranges toward Vicenza; our own area came to be almost a little federated province, well-governed and highly civilized, on the periphery of this kingdom.

Tar still held me in esteem, and showed respect for us all. He came along to see us with Aquila,* one of his lieutenants —in other words Rino. There were many Aquilas up in the mountains, including several White Aquilas and Black Aquilas. Aquila-Rino was dressed modestly, and armed with discretion. He only had a sten gun and two grenades, and naturally the sharp dagger in his stocking. His hair was smooth and combed with care, and he had quite long whiskers. Tar was splendid; his whiskers were longer and thicker than his lieutenants'; he was hardly armed at all, he just had an ancient, infallible pistol slung negligently from his belt. He wore shorts, high boots, and this colonial helmet. Everything about him was splendid, his dark face, his soft velvet eyes, his white teeth, the fine features of his face, his elegant gestures.

One day we were presented with a turkey; the peasants prepared a banquet, and we invited Tar and Aquila. Unfortunately toward evening I had one of those headaches which I used to get every now and then at that time, so I could not participate. I spent the evening lying in the bushes in front of the house, part of the time listening to the talk of the guests. Our whole squad was there, the peasant girls and the guests; moreover at the last minute they were joined by Enrico's brother and father. This strange visit

* I.e., Eagle.

218

was quite exceptional; Enrico's father had suddenly got it into his head that he must sec what his son was doing up in the mountains. The brother had hurriedly sent word that we should hide some of the weapons, so as not to frighten him too much.

The evening was very gay; the two guests were presented to Enrico's father, who was a director of a large firm at Valdagno. He greeted them with great courtesy. "Aquila?" he said. "That doesn't seem a local name to me . . ."

He liked Tar and wanted him to sit on his right. I heard snatches of conversation.

"First I got rid of the Fascist Commissar," said Tar, "then the son of the Commissar."

"What do you mean 'got rid'?" asked Enrico's father.

Enrico intervened politely: "Some more wine, Father?"

The night was wet with dew. I heard the rattle of crockery and the calm words.

"You put a circle of thin wire around the head . . .

"And with these pincers you give a turn . . .

"And at the second turn . . .

"And at the third, when the bones of the head go *cric* . . ."

We began to hear of Christian Democrat units; they were a little late in the day perhaps, but anyway here they were. The participation of priests and some of the churchgoing folk in the first phases of the Resistance had been admirable; but now this somewhat tardy, organized intervention made one think that there was an essence of competitive opportunism.

A great chief of these Guelphlike neo-partisans emerged; he was called Omobono and operated in an area not far from ours. One day his visit was announced; he came in the afternoon without an escort; it was Robertino, our ex-school friend Robertino, with long brown hair combed back. Surprise was succeeded by a wave of discourteous hilarity;

everyone pointed a finger, shaking with laughter, at him. "And so you are Omobono? Just imagine, Omobono is Robertino!"

He hadn't stayed with us at school many years, because he couldn't get through his exams; he got up very early in the morning to study, and studied practically the whole day at his desk. His father used to come up on tiptoe, searching for the comic paper inevitably hidden among the books, then gave him the first clout, ruffling the long brown hair. "*Muoviti, scuotiti!* Go on, get going!" cried the father like somebody advising a basic remedy, a radical cure, though with little hope of success.

What with all these clouts, Robertino had a curious scholastic career. Eventually, I simply don't know how, he found himself on a course for *bersaglieri* officers; there was nobody there to clout him, so he found himself in difficulty again, poor fellow. People who were with him remember that, when he had an evening pass, he would sometimes be found standing by the barracks window on the second floor as if he was wondering whether that might be the best way out. He was a good boy, sincerely keen to do his best; he had large gray eyes, which filled with tears, like big springs of water, at the vagaries of life's harsh ways.

When he came to see us at our camp above Isola, more than one of us felt that the Catholics' great endeavor to catch up with the rest of Italy was not beginning under good auspices. If things go on like this, I thought, the Catholic party will become the party of those who can't pass their exams: the *Muoviti, scuotiti* party. Of course in Italy now we are all very content to be in the hands of those in whose hands we are; but at that time, on that hot afternoon, as we sat on the grass next to Omobono, whose big eyes overflowed with the usual lake of tears, we very nearly began to weep too about the birth of the neo-Guelph ruling class.

The new partisan levies matured at the same time as the first fruits and the summer harvests. Recruits arrived, and we went to receive them in the early hours of the night, at various points on the hills. They came in little groups from the towns and villages; for the most part they were young, they had left their homes and families only a few hours before; they had been conducted to the foot of the hills by appropriate messengers, then sent up a path. They would suddenly be challenged as they reached a corner, and then perhaps the boyish illusion of playing at war would be tinged with a certain element of anxiety. After that we'd take them over. We would explain the orographic layout of the area, what other units there were in that neighborhood, what weapons we had. Finally we would tell them: "You'll get used to it all very quickly." To get them used to it all we would give them something to do, even on the first day—a little expedition to the plain, a mission to a neighboring unit. Berto arrived one night, with a friend, and in the morning we sent them to Negro to fetch some magazines.

They left at a good pace, humming tunes from a song. We could see they were well-brought-up boys, punctual at mass and all that, though not by any means bigoted: typical products of our Vicenza Sunday schools. It was difficult to evaluate their interest in the Resistance. Berto says that, when he reached us that time, I—being the first to receive him—said to him severely, after the initial welcomes: "Why are you here?" and he, taken by surprise, not knowing what else to say, and hoping to please me, said: "For the flag of the Fatherland." Unfortunately I was in a bad mood, and said even more severely: "And what does the flag of the Fatherland mean to you?" Berto, adjusting himself at once, said: "I don't care a fig for it." And I asked, with extreme severity: "Why?" Here Berto stopped answering and thought to himself: This band is just a bunch of questioners.

Anyhow these two started off toward the Torreselle ridge on their first modest job as partisans, humming their tunes halfway through the morning. They returned very pale in the late afternoon.

They had been given a cordial welcome at Negro's unit. It was a picturesque setting; there was a bit of a fuss going on, because they had been meaning to issue shirts that morning. "You can watch, if you like," said the Commissar. The shirts had been dropped from the sky, with the weapons and the Canadian cheese; they were the usual British military shirts, the ones made of khaki cloth, with the attractive pockets. Berto and his companion were still dressed in civilian clothes and were half hoping to benefit from the issue too. An orderly called a meeting, and the partisans came flocking up, grouping themselves in front of Negro and the Commissar.

The Commissar began to speak in his negligent way, and officially announced the issue of the shirts. "We are a bit short of shoes too," he said, "but anyhow let's begin with the shirts." He himself was in slippers made of cinder-colored terry cloth; he was always like that, and they added to his negligent air. He was a rickety man, who dragged his feet and his words; his hands were resting on the small, special, rather exotic machine gun that was hanging across his chest.

"Now that you're here," he said, "we'll take the opportunity of checking weapons for Brigade Command. It's a formality."

The orderlies began to go around, and the partisans handed in their weapons. Suddenly there was a bustle, noises, a confusion, as of cattle being driven. The group of disarmed partisans formed themselves into a semicircle; in the middle—between three or four guards, pointing rifles at them—stood two men, also disarmed and with their hands up.

They were obviously brothers, not young, very well built. The barrels of the rifles were arranged in an arc; the Commissar took a few steps forward. Now he pivoted on the heel of his left foot, and as he spoke he punctuated his words with the point of his gray terry cloth slipper. "Gio-

222

vanni Riale and Saverio Riale, guilty of theft, condemned to death. The execution will take place immediately."

The brothers were shouting. *"Dio ladro!"* they cried, which is calling God a thief, and a common blasphemy.

The Commissar was shouting, too: *"Dio boia!"* he cried, which is also quite common, and is like calling God a hangman, or an executioner.

Then they exchanged shouts.

Brothers Riale: *"Dio boia!"*

Commissar: *"Dio ladro!"*

Together: *"Dio ladro! Dio boia!"*

Now the Commissar was firing; the two brothers began to sink, then crumpled up, gurgling.

Berto's knees knocked together so hard that he thought that they would become audible.

The Commissar shuffled back a couple of paces and said to him: "Aim not bad, eh?," then gave orders for the weapons to be handed back. Berto looked at the face of his friend, which was white; next he glanced quickly at the two brothers, stretched out on the ground with their faces upturned and eyes open: on their chest they had dark patches that were growing larger.

This was how the shirts were issued; and it must have made a great impression on Berto and his friend, because, during the period that they were with us, they jumped whenever it was announced that rations or clothing were going to be issued.

The day would be full of events. The stolen vehicles would arrive at first light. We had to unload the spoils of war, then make the vehicles disappear. The consignment arrived on the asphalt road in full enemy territory, in front of the old cemetery at Isola. To get rid of the vehicles we had to drive them through the fields along unsuitable lanes; sometimes they would slip off a rustic bridge and end in a ditch, which meant we had to dismantle them piece by piece, and carry them away in the form of spare parts.

Then there were the normal activities of the day, such as the visits to Tar's headquarters. He would receive us seated on the ground and playing the guitar, while nearby there would be some prisoner also seated on the ground and stripped to the waist. A leather belt would be hanging from a branch; a lieutenant would be shaving in front of a mirror hanging from another branch.

There were long trips into the hills, to make contact with the partisans in the farthest areas, the Val dell'Agno, the mountains of Recoaro. Every trip was an adventure; one continually met people who wanted to arrest one, to confiscate one's weapons, or shoot one with theirs.

There were staff meetings for planning attacks, rapid training courses in the use of plastic explosives, inspections, visits. People came from all over to consult us, as if we were mountain oracles. Some asked us for military advice, others for moral advice; some brought us the good wishes of the seminary, others feelers from the police, others still other things. We all worked as consultants in audience hours; bores and souls in distress came too, and these we handed on to Gigi, because he was patient and tolerant.

We made our raids at night. We entered, pistol in hand certainly, but asking permission; we asked the family seated at supper not to be afraid; there was a curious moment of reciprocal embarrassment; then we explained the legal nature of the operation, and got going. Severino would run his eyes over the feet of the men, because his shoes were worn out and he always hoped to find someone with feet the same size as his. Sometimes the feet would be nearly right, and in the course of the raid Severino would try on their shoes, but never with any luck.

There were also the nights when we would go off to blow up railway tracks, to ambush depots of Nazi jam or damage superannuated planes at the Villaverla airfield, or to try to bump off Fascist brigands. The evening they burned the houses at Santomio, three of us went down to San Vito to remove a couple of Fascists. They looked like bats, bats which seem like birds when they are flying but miserable pieces of rag when on the ground. We stripped them and tied them together, back to back, then left them on a dung-heap belonging to one of the first houses we came across at San Vito, on the side nearest the mountain.

By now Severino was practically shoeless; what was left of his soles folded under his feet and stopped him from walking properly. So he, Raffaele, and I went down to Val-di-là, under Monte Pulgo, hoping that some large German would pass by. As our race did not seem to produce feet of the required size, we counted on German blood.

The two who did arrive were gigantic. They were driving an almost archaic wagon, drawn by an archaic horse; in it were two or three half-filled sacks. They were old peasants with mustaches; they didn't seem as if they were soldiers but were more like millers, or perhaps muleteers, for all the world as though they came from some valley not unlike Val-di-là.

When they came to the spot where we were waiting, flat on our stomachs among the bushes, they stopped, got off right in front of us and began to urinate, one of them toward the little valley, the other practically on our faces. I was right in front, and between me and the German there was a semitransparent barrier of acacia leaves; his face was on a level with mine, not more than a couple of feet away, but he had his eyes down, as one does when one is urinating. I kept still; if he raises his eyes, I thought, he will see mine in the middle of the acacia leaves, right in front of his nose, and then I shall have to fire, and good-by to him; otherwise I'll never shoot at these pissing Germans. Severino and Raffaele must have had the same thought;

the fact was that when the Germans had finished and gone, Severino put another piece of string around his shoe, and we returned to camp.

It was always a problem whether or not to fire at people in cold blood, especially from behind a hedge. One part of our conscience told us that it was an explicit duty; but the other shut itself off in a sort of obstinate silence. To kill in hot blood, *per incidens,* is nothing. We were walking one night along a mountain path, Gios and I, in Valstagna; at a bend in the path, about two yards away, there was a tremendous flash, and we were caught in a sort of wind, a ball of chaos; we flung ourselves face downward on the pebbles of the path and began firing like mad, up toward the bend. Then we realized that the things rolling down toward us were two dead men; this we didn't mind at all, we had done well and they had done badly.

Killing properly was when we killed a German boy, on the Altipiano. He had said that he had deserted to join us, and was with us for some time, then he tried to escape, and was captured, and after a while he confessed that he was a spy. There was nothing else but to kill him. We were all in agreement about this, even he. He was twenty years old, fair-haired. We tied his hands with rope, in this little rocky dip.

We had to ask the fair-haired boy whether he wanted us to give a message to someone at his home in Germany— we would pass it on, assuming that we ourselves would still be alive at the end of the war. He hesitated a little and then said no. We asked whom he wanted to stay with him, and he chose one of us. The others went away.

Bees were buzzing; it was late in the season for them.

"Are you afraid?" He was so young that it was natural to address him as *tu.*

"Not much."

Both stood up, almost touching. Would it not be best for him to turn around? He had thought of this too, but he shook his head. "Shut your eyes," and while he was shutting them, the finger had already started to press the trigger, one closed one's eyes too, and in a kind of pulse blended with the color of the day, one lost that innermost thing that one considers to be oneself, and it seemed like dying together.

That was killing.

When walking across the plain by day we had to go almost entirely through sorghum. The countryside was like a chessboard, and we moved from one square to the other. From up above, the chessboard appeared brilliant, rational; but as we went down into it we couldn't find our way about any more, and it was necessary to be empirically logical and follow the lines of the trees, the big festoons of the vines, the walls along the fields. Noises, voices came to us as if flying or swimming in the air, detached from history; we felt absurd in the middle of this great placid machine which continued forever to produce leaves, polenta, grapes.

The crickets, in August, began calling when the light dimmed, toward seven in the evening, and the little hills turned blue. The air cooled, the Fascist brigands returned to their lairs, the children shouted on the threshing floors, in war as they do in peace, and the dogs barked gaily among the children. Bats came out like little bundles, fluttering round and round, the last birds went to roost and twittered to one another before going to sleep. There was smoke above the houses. As we sat on the ground, with rifles between our knees, it seemed as though the countryside was watching over us as if we were its children.

The rose-colored reflections faded gently in the air. The colors became denser; we saw the specter of a great turquoise lake forming high above us and mirroring the dark lake of the sorghum. The countryside disappeared in a surge of dim waves; we felt as though we were in a tide, and began to perceive the slow, slow turn of the earth, the absurd grandeur of its crust on which we were placed, defenseless against what was forming overhead. For a little the distant shapes of the mountains gave us company, gave scale to things; then they too disappeared, swallowed up in the lake, and we didn't see anything more, except the sky.

There was a blackout in the villages, so there were no reflections from artificial lights; thus the sky commanded the whole countryside. We lay stretched out on our backs. Even to speak had an odd effect, the acoustics of the sky at night are very strange; one hears one's voice, but it loses all quality and becomes bodiless. Dante knew the names of the stars and of the constellations, and spoke them up into the air; the sky drank his words.

The summer was too luxuriant; we could feel the season weakening under its very ripeness. I had gone to drink at a spring which rose halfway down the hill. I was hot, and was worried about some news which had reached me from the plain; then I had one of those moments of inner disquiet which came over me every now and then in the course of that summer—when I seriously lost the sense of the *wherefore* of what we were doing, and the countryside became sibylline, vaguely hallucinatory. Avidly I drank the clear, fresh water, until I was satiated, then I went away a few paces from the spring into the trees. I lay down on the ground looking up at the trembling leaves, and after a little shut my eyes almost without realizing it; and so, lying there on the grass with summer's minuscule noises going on all round me, I went to sleep, with one hand on my tommy gun and the other flat on the ground, open and with the palm upward. As I slept it seemed as if something fell from the branches above into my palm but I knew at once that it was not, for instance, a bird dropping, it was much lighter, though not so light as a leaf. Then suddenly I realized what it was. It was a cicada. I wanted to open my eyes again to make sure, but a curious idea occurred to me, which was that I'd never even seen a cicada, so even looking wouldn't prove anything.

It was strange that all through my childhood in the country I had never seen a cicada; it was not that I hadn't been *able* to see one; all I had had to do was to climb a tree where one was calling and look for it, because one knows they don't fly away but just stop calling and remain where they are. The truth was that even as a child I hadn't *wanted* to see one, for some indefinite reason, associated with a sense of sacrilege. It may perhaps have been because of the way they have of calling, which through a bizarre acoustical effect at one stage seems to be a web of thin cries just a little distance from the ear, and at another an unfathomable choir as large as all the countryside; there is no perspective in the cries of cicadas. The fact is that I had never seen cicadas, neither in life nor in pictures.

The cicada must without doubt be Greek. It is inconceivable that the Greeks should not have felt how mysterious it is: they had an incredible ear for mysteries. How does one say "cicada" in Greek? And how old is it biologically? Older than man, than the dog? Why didn't they teach us these things, at school? The bloody bastards, I said to myself (but without much conviction, because it was hot), it seems as if they did their best not to teach us anything interesting—they might at least have taught us Greek properly. Here I am with this thing on my hand that has fallen from a tree, and even if it is in fact a cicada what do I know about it? Nothing, not even its name in Greek.

Voices woke me. They were people coming to drink at the spring. Gradually as they spoke I recognized them. There were three.

"The important thing is to stay alive," said Enrico. Then he praised the water and said something about the pleasure of being able to drink as much as one wanted.

"When the war's over, I'm going to do everything I've always longed to do."

"Aren't you the son of the Director at Marzotto's?" asked Negro.

"Yes," said Enrico. "What about you? What do your people do?"

"Nothing," said Negro. "They've been dead for as long as I can remember."

"I'm sorry," said Enrico.

"However, when the war's over I'm also going to do things I've always longed to do," said Negro.

"I must finish my studies," said Raffaele. "Because my family has made so many sacrifices to let me study."

"You go rock-climbing, don't you?" asked Enrico. Raffaele said: "Yes," and Enrico said: "Then after the war you'll have to take me. I've a mad drive to go rock-climbing."

"The first thing I want is to own a motorcycle," said Negro. "A red Saturno that goes at eighty, even ninety."

"I want to dedicate myself a little more seriously to women," said Enrico. "And I want to get this climbing out of my system."

Now that I have thought over this conversation again and have reconstructed the sentences, I can quite see that there was nothing unusual about it, but at that time it did seem unusual. As I only heard the voices, they seemed in another sphere of reality, like speaking ghosts; and as it happens that all three of them are dead, they *are* in fact ghosts now.

I lay there with my eyes closed until they had gone away, without calling out to them. Then I sat up on the grass and looked in the palm of my open hand; there was nothing there at all, so I shut it, and I thought: When you shut your hand all you do is take a fistful of air.

We had booked the Major for the Feast of the Assumption. He was the biggest of our ethical-political victims; it was also the longest of our expeditions into the plain, because we had to go through almost half the province, and pass through the high sorghum. We had been, one could say, his pupils in the youth organizations of the Fascist regime; we felt the need to resolve his case personally. He was an important and well-known figure, one of those who publicly demanded two or three times a week that someone (usually us) should be shot. We knew that every evening, toward sunset, he passed on a bicycle along a lane outside Vicenza, making for the village where he was billeted with a family.

The expedition lasted several days. The first night we traveled through sorghum and country lanes, deeper and deeper into the open plain, which stretched toward the east and south. Then, after a day or two in unknown territory, we found the place and asked a family of peasants to put us up. I think they were people who knew one of us, or perhaps they knew some member of our families; in Italy one always gets on through acquaintances. The fact was that these peasants, especially the women, were simply delighted with us. They believed in the omnipotence of the partisans, and of us in particular; they were convinced that we could do anything, and when Venus appeared in the evening over the distant hills, they were sure that it was a signal for us, and it was completely useless to deny it. They didn't have an atom of fear about the risks they ran in giving us hospitality in their house, they were so proud to have us there, they thought it such an honor.

There were four or five of us, all with tommy guns, because we wanted to kill the Major collectively; except Gigi, who being an antimilitarist had the job of burying him, and followed with a spade. The house was a couple of miles from the point which we had chosen on the road; the country was irregular, all furrowed with ditches and canals, and going there was difficult and hazardous. It is quite a job killing a man. The evening before the feast day we were at our posts among the bushes, a good hour before sunset, because the Major usually arrived at sunset. We had brought a watermelon and divided it up among us. Some working-girls returned home along the road from the factory, on bicycles, and they said: "What a lovely smell of watermelon." We stayed there absolutely still, with our mouths full. This will be the last smell that the Major smells, I thought. We kept our eyes on the straight bit of road at the end of which he was expected to appear; we had drawn lots for the order of fire.

Sunset came, then evening. Some cyclists passed, for the most part different from the Major, either in sex or girth, so there was no cause for a false alarm; one or two did run some danger, though.

Very soon it was dark, and we realized that the Major would not pass. Late at night we decided to go away and sleep in the fields near the house belonging to our peasants; it was a beautiful night with a huge moon, but the way was just as difficult, because of the watercourses which continually crossed the road.

Beyond a magnificent meadow, really marvelous under the moon, there was quite a large ditch. As far as we could see, there was no trace of a bridge either to right or left; maybe we'd have to walk for miles to find one.

"We must get over this ditch," I said.

Nobody was very enthusiastic, and I was a little uncertain about how to do it.

"Let's go and look for a bridge," said Dante. "No," I said, "we'll cross here," and I went straight into the water. In two paces I had gone down up to my neck; with the third pace I disappeared, except for my hands holding the tommy gun. I must confess that ditches frighten me, but I was so annoyed that I went on walking, even under the water, and in time I came up, on the other side. The others joined me half an hour afterward, having found a bridge a little farther down. I had taken off all my clothes and was running around a reed hut on which I had put them to dry in the moonlight. They didn't get at all dry, so Gigi lent me his vest, which was without sleeves, and I put it on upside down instead of trousers. Thus we arrived at our sorghum fields, and I put on my clothes, still very wet, and we went to sleep.

The following day we returned to the road an hour before sunset. A cyclist appeared at the end of the road, and I saw immediately that it was the Major. We were lying among bushes, with our tommy guns at the alert; the Major came forward, all absorbed in his thoughts; dressed thus in civilian clothes, he appeared depressed and weak; slowly I shifted my tommy gun, following the advancing Major so that the circle of my foresight was kept a little in front. When I reached the right point I stopped, and in a moment I saw him coming into the foresight, with his sad thoughts; and there, in the tiny iron circle, I now wish to leave him.

The summer became a confused period of merrymaking, in that moment of anarchy which precedes the end. From our ridges we seemed to feel the land move, as if Italy, down below, was splitting. How does that verse go? *I have no senses: or sense. I have no limits.* There were no limits any more; the points of reference waved up and down as on a ship. Extrovert bands of partisans arrived from everywhere, for the most part in transit; usually they didn't even come up to the ridge, but stayed at the foot of the hill, like goats stripping it of leaves. Only the heads, the adventurous and wandering chiefs of staff, visited us. It was enough just to look at them to see how different we were. It seemed that a new mutation had arrived, a product of some other culture. They had silk sashes, fancy machine guns, gay and terrible faces.

They seemed like people on the stage. Italy was splitting open and spewing out these droves of fancy-dress people. It was as if they were preparing for a grand finale, some big costume film.

Extraordinary things happened; the deputy head of the Vicenza police asked us for an appointment and came up to Monte Viale with his minions, and we went along without minions because we were our own minions, and we all met in an inn. We put our rifles in a corner, so as to be polite, ordered white wine, and began our discussion. They came to offer collaboration, protection for political prisoners, and the like, in exchange for certain assurances for their own persons at the end of the war. They negotiated well, in a somewhat corrupt manner. In effect they put themselves in our hands, but they did it stylishly. I had always understood that the civil war separated the two factions like a sacrament, "an indelible sign that can never be erased." Clearly I was wrong.

I did not, however, explain it to them. It was the moment of strange happenings, like a dress rehearsal for the end of the war. Moreover, it was disconcerting to be considered important; I felt like saying: "Look, we're just private people, and we don't mean to *count* at the end of the war." However, it seemed a pity to disappoint them.

Then came September with the first grapes, and the confusion became menacing. There were big *rastrellamenti* in the mountains and arrests in the villages, houses were burned, and there were some executions; the brigands, abandoned by their constables, became more and more ferocious. Here too an equilibrium was upset, and all was disorder. They also took away the Count, who was, among the chiefs of the plain, not only a firm friend but our indispensable support. Rules were discarded, and we found ourselves empirically rushing in all directions, trying to find ways of responding in kind to such brutality. I had always dreamed about the true empirical war, the giving and taking of real life; and now I found myself in the middle of it.

Behind the hedge, between Isola and Santomio. Lying in

234

an ambush, eyes on the distant turning of the road. A wagon-load of prisoners was about to arrive from Isola. For artistic reasons we knew we oughtn't to involve ourselves in such carnage as this; but it wasn't the moment for art: to hell with art. The road was completely empty, the sun burning down on the asphalt. A shadow moved at the corner in the distance and a puppy came trotting along waving the stump of its tail, and behind the puppy, a priest came slowly forward reading his breviary, all black in the hot sun. Behind him there was nobody. The puppy sped by, Enrico ran out, stopped the priest, and we saw him inquire about those to be slaughtered. The priest made a movement with his hands which seemed to say: "Ah, my son, they must just have gone by." Enrico knelt on the asphalt and we saw him utter blasphemies with hands raised to heaven. The priest listened attentively, made the sign of the cross, and went on.

Marching toward San Vito, where they held the Count—if he was still alive. A great demonstrative action was under way, in which all our units in the area were taking part. It was early afternoon, already the whole arc of the hills was full of the sound of shooting, and we were hurrying along so as to be in time to take our part in the glory. People were encouraging us as they do at football matches: *"Bravi! Bravi!* Let 'em have it!" We went in and out of courtyards, doorways, kitchen gardens, almost through two rows of people cheering us on.

On the mountains above San Vito, Gigi and I, having been detached from the others during a *rastrellamento*, determined to build up a battalion in memory of the Count. The peasants in the hamlets, awaiting their fate, grouped in front of their houses, reciting their rosaries.

The summer was coming to an end; our sense that the land was shifting under our feet had passed; the country-side began to lose color. The gangs of extrovert types had disappeared, the *rastrellamenti* had died down, and we moved among the last sorghum fields in the plain performing our little tired actions. We spent earthy, granulous hours in the great sorghum fields. We knew all the phenomena of the green underworld: the damp earth, the watery stalks, the frail tufts of the corncobs. We had fantasies of being creatures of the sorghum too; we learned how to walk underneath it on all fours, how to stay there in conversation, how to sleep there at night.

"It will be a disaster when they cut the sorghum."

"Perhaps they won't cut it this year."

"Soon it will all be dry."

"Then we'll have to go away."

"Where can we go?"

We began to think of the winter. The previous winter some of us had been in hiding, some of us had stayed at home. There is snow in the mountains, in winter; there wouldn't be any more leaves on the hills. Our war depended on leaves.

"Do you think we'll have to go through another winter?"

"Who knows?"

I didn't care about anything any more. The leaves were already beginning to die. And there were also the dogs, with which certain enemy units went on search parties among the fields. I had a special knife for these dogs, halfway between a pruning knife and a scimitar. A friend who had come up to see us had given it to me, with his best wishes for a good war to which this was supposed to be his contribution; he assured me that it was perfect for dogs. All you had to do was this: lie on the ground face upward, wait for your dog to rush madly overhead momentarily exposing its stomach; then a thrust, in the right spot, and *frun*, it would be split from top to bottom. Mechanically I tried to believe him, and I nearly succeeded. All the same, the knife kept me good company in the sorghum, and I am still convinced it was very good against dogs.

The Berici Hills are behind Vicenza, to the south; they have tiny, almost miniature slopes, which form valleys and creeks. In one of them there is a sad lake called Fimón; two shaggy watersheds diverged above the lake like spread-out legs. Midway through autumn we were there, between the thighs. The ground is chalky, curled all over with groups of chestnut trees; there are a few isolated houses. It was a strange thought that people should spend all their lives there. They were so poor, one just couldn't understand how they lived. They said they were peasants, but where were the fields? The men had their various jobs to do, either up in the woods or in the boggy area near the lake. The women made children and soup, and fetched water in buckets, and cooked polenta.

Yet these people were in so many ways the same as us. They laughed, for example, in the same way as we did; they spoke the same language, though usually in a rather coarser manner, and with an effect that was somewhat like shouting; but in conversation—once we were inside their sparsely furnished houses—their voices softened, and one began to distinguish underneath concepts and emotions which worked in the same way as our own.

Where did they go to church, to school? Who came up here to look after them, if they got ill? When they had to go down to the city, they went barefoot with their shoes in their hands; they put them on before entering the Porta Monte.

Their comparative gaiety disconcerted me.

"One should go around looking definitely gloomy while there are Italians living in such conditions," I said to Bene.

"You'd have a gloomy-looking nation living around groups of comparatively gay valley people," he replied.

"If I were born here, I'd be a terrorist," I said.

"Aren't you one already?"

Together we analyzed the possibility of exploiting the resources of the valley in a better way. There were all these chestnuts on the ground, and still more up in the trees. Why didn't they go into the plain to sell them? We put this question to the peasants, and they replied: "Because nobody wants them." We pictured a row of little factories for making chestnut jam under the slopes; and we imagined the valley booming and prosperous, and the people with shoes. But then the houses would be abandoned, the valley would be left empty.

Yet I saw very well that these houses were not just shelters, they were part of a way of life, and so was everything else, the enclosures between the chestnut trees, the paths, the cowsheds, the archways; and it struck me that the poverty was inseparable from the rest, and this no doubt was true of Italian life in general; poverty could not be removed without dismantling Italian life as we knew it.

I said to Bene: "To root out poverty they'll have to destroy Italy."

"Don't exaggerate," said Bene.

We spent a lot of time lying on our backs on straw. We were the lazy ones at Fimón. Idly we dreamed of inventing a new form of war, and meanwhile we played cards. There was no longer a screen of leaves between us and the world: there were only twigs and stubble in the fields. We sensed the chalk under the rotting leaves. We felt muddy and chalky ourselves, and also exposed.

"We're badly situated here," we said. We seemed visible to everybody; so as to conceal ourselves a little better, we gradually climbed into the space between the thighs of the valley, right to the end of it. At the very summit of the valley, below the brow, beyond which there ran a road, was a low chalky cave, where we ended up hiding ourselves. It rained. We understood what it must have been like for the first men, or monkeys even, the prehuman monkeys, when they were reduced to about half a dozen, and the cold began and they looked out dejectedly from the mouth of a cave like this one, which must have seemed to them, too, the entrance to the womb of the earth, into which there was no alternative but to return as the seasons—and life itself—were gradually being extinguished.

"We must leave this valley." And early in November, when people commemorate the dead, we began to make our preparations. Our little band, which had been so perfect, was disbanded; it snapped open and sent us shooting off like buttons; we scattered, young itinerant masters, alone now or in couples, and we journeyed through the provinces dispensing the salt of our mastery.

Marietto and I left the rim of the lake on our bicycles, by the path through the fields. We went part of the way together, up to where the asphalt roads began, the hostile main roads, in the very plain itself. We had false papers, and felt a bit uncomfortable. I began to recite verses by Gozzano, whose technique I admired, but Marietto (who thought poetry frivolous) listened with little enthusiasm.

We had come to the last stretch, we could see the traffic on the main road; once more we checked the time and place for our rendezvous at Padua, the site of our new assignment, and off we went, he one way and I another.

The warrior in repose reads books and lies full length on a couch. He eats zabaglione and receives visitors in secret. One day some men arrived whom I did not know. I saw them from the study on the first floor; they were coming along the road and talking to one another with their hands in the pockets of their overcoats. Marta went to open the door; when I heard the voice of the chief visitor, at the entrance, I thought at once: Help! I had to do something, so I locked my door from the inside, and put the key in my pocket. Then I threw my wallet into the stove. The idea of not letting them find us with papers was part of an acknowledged technique; but it was also a bit of a mania with us; there was certainly no necessity to burn the *whole* wallet, with my ten lire inside, which was all I had. The balcony looked out over a terrace enclosed with wire netting; behind the netting was one of the visitors, waiting

with a revolver in his hand. I had no weapons—the warrior
in repose had got rid of them before starting on his repose—
and I felt very much in a trap. Downstairs the visitors were
going through each room in turn, and every time they locked
the doors. My room above was already locked; which promised a ridiculous situation.

"Little goose, little goose, please will you open?"

"No, I won't."

"Please will you open?"

"No, I won't."

"Please will you open?"

And then what? I could even open. The chief visitor had
now finished the ground floor, and had carefully locked
all the doors; he called in the sentinels so that they could
come upstairs in force with him. I peeped out of the window
of the balcony; I saw the man with the revolver turn around
to enter the house, and when he had disappeared I went
out onto the parapet, tied my blue silk scarf to a bar on the
railing, let myself down to the end of the scarf and dropped.
I was already practically on the ground, and there was
hardly any distance to go; but then as I scrambled over
the netting I got tangled up in barbed wire, and so as not
to tear my clothes too much I allowed myself to fall rather
clumsily on the other side. It was one of those falls which
could break a leg; and indeed I limped a bit as I ran
through the fields.

The house was on a hill; the fields around it were on a
slope, so that the house overlooked a great stretch of countryside—even more so at that season when there were no
crops. I ran a long way, feeling very visible; they didn't
see me, because when they went through the rooms, methodically going into each one, they didn't bother to look out
of the windows.

I was wearing the only civilian piece of clothing that I
had left at that time; it was the sort of thing one would
wear to a party, a double-breasted suit with dark brown

stripes, of very nice smooth material, in almost mint condition except for those recent tears from the barbed wire. The fields were dry and bare from the late autumn, furrowed from plowing; I ran energetically in this dark double-breasted suit, dragging my leg. I couldn't see the house any more. I remembered my blue silk scarf, and it seemed obvious to me that I would be followed. There were some corn shocks, and I hid myself in one of these; there was hardly enough room, even when I was sitting with my knees up. If they come this way, I thought, let's hope they won't want to look inside the shocks. I hadn't thought about the possibility of their having a dog. I thought of this dog when I heard barking about a hundred yards away. Here they come, I said to myself; I could also hear a man's voice calling to the dog. Let them come, I thought; I'm not going to move again. I was almost looking forward to a spell in jail.

The dog had found me, there was no doubt of it. I could tell from the way it was barking, and in fact it was not long before it arrived and began barking furiously at the shock. The man took the sheaves apart and found me inside.

But he was not the visitor I expected, he was a peasant. "I'm sorry to be a nuisance," I said, and he said: "May God strike the whole lot dead," then he put the sheaves back and went away with his dog. So I took up my warrior's repose again and slept inside the shock until evening; then I set off once more through the fields. After a few hours I arrived in a safe area. I went to a farm belonging to some people I knew. As it was night, I didn't want to disturb them, so I climbed into the hayloft and, since I was cold, buried myself entirely in the hay, and this put me into very great danger, because in the morning my peasant friends came with pitchforks to take the hay away, and they stuck these forks with tremendous vigor into the hay (I had seen them do it, take the hay from the loft, so many times) until they unearthed a shoe, and when they tried to lift this shoe with the point of a fork they found a leg, and attached to the leg was a young man in a brown striped double-breasted suit, asleep under the hay; so they woke me up and we greeted one another.

I know now that Marta, when the Fascists had reached the door of the locked study on the first floor, said that she didn't have the key, which was true, because I had it in my pocket; so they gave her a dose of electric shock (they had brought a portable machine), then tore down the door. And later, because of my blue silk scarf, they gave her another dose of electric shock and some cigarette burns too. But she didn't tell them my name. She was a good girl, Marta: she told them the first two syllables and changed the others. She even persuaded herself that she had told them, so she didn't have to say any more. However, later on, in prison, they inflicted far worse tortures on her, those syphilitic, impotent bastards.

10

In the city, the people went about their own business. There were bars, cinemas, trolley cars, newspapers: it all seemed crazy. At first we regarded it as the kingdom of Satan; the pavements were hot, the faces of people walking along the pavements made us jump; and the fine clothes, the overcoats, the ties, filled us with both disgust and fear. Padua seemed a great sink of iniquity; we had to take care not to assume instinctively that all her citizens were traitors, that the whole complex of doorways, arcades, bars, sewers, barracks, trolley lines, simply represented a world that had to be exterminated. Quite probably we had a touch of that usual resentment that ex-servicemen feel. Old university friends would meet us on the street and say: "My dear, I haven't seen you for ages! Have you done your Romance Philology? Have you done your Medieval History, Part II?" They must have felt surprised at our obvious desire to hurry away from them; they annoyed us, but our behavior was not just due to that.

I had never felt so much of an outlaw as I did then, when I returned to the world of everyday, with my forged papers. In normal wars both sides have worlds of their own going on behind the lines. But now it seemed all one-sided to me; the trolleys were Fascist, as were the Post Office, the shops, the air-raid shelters, the ration cards—everything.

I began to feel that basically I detested society altogether —not just this one in particular, but every society that was urbanized and therefore capable of producing Fascism. Bestial cohabitations of so-called civilized men, I said to myself. Loathsome parasites, one and all. Suck your own loathsome blood, cohabit. And all praise to our own Thebaid, where we searched for water in the rocky valleys, and the crow brought us polenta and margarine. Sinners, whoremongers, sodomites, do your beastly deeds: go to your homes and couple with your bitches, couple with your trolleys. Go to your solemn masses, stick holy candles up your ass.

In fact, we were rather afraid of the world, at first. The people in the streets seemed extremely fearsome; instinctively we looked for machine guns in the hands of the milkmen, of women at the news stands. The first time we entered a restaurant all the men sitting at the tables looked like black Fascists to us, they all seemed to exude that repellent attitude that these people had when they donned civilian clothes. In a few weeks we got used to it; soon we went to places frequented by functionaries of the Ministries, the police department, even the torture houses; we even went there on purpose to look at them.

We worked at the "Center" at Padua. A clandestine Center is a most peculiar thing: the closer one gets to it, the less one sees it. From afar nobody doubted that it was a solid and tangible organization, that it hammered out directives and was altogether imposing. But then, as one got nearer, all that happened was that one got caught up in a net of precarious and laborious contacts. Actually it wasn't even a net: just certain people (with false names) intent on weaving it. At first I thought that in the middle of it all there must be, sitting there like a spider, some sort of living Center, invisible in its silken web. But was it really there? After a while I began to understand that the net itself was the Center, and that it was being constantly torn and as constantly mended. So long as some of the threads were there, the thing kept going.

The Center was subtly though irregularly in touch with the entire region. Almost all of us worked in this liaison business, whether at Padua or elsewhere in the Veneto; some of us were full-timers, others were only temporaries. Now we realized that liaison work was not just an important aspect of the Resistance, but the Resistance itself. When it was decided that some liaising had to be done, a whole lot of things automatically ensued, *comitati* were created, newspapers were distributed, the financial side was worked out, messages were sent out or received, orders were given and put into effect. You just had to say you wanted to do some liaising and all the rest followed.

A certain amount of our energy was taken up with liaising among ourselves, but quite a bit was also left over for liaising with other people. We went about with false papers and permits; some of us (especially Marietto and myself, as we were actually living in Padua) often changed our domicile as well as our identities. Sometimes I took a few years off my age and made myself into a seventeen-year-old who had just matriculated and was still exempt from military service; on other occasions I advanced my age and made myself a member of a military unit in some remote part of the country, and would grant myself both ordinary and extraordinary permits.

I also carried the Steyr in my inside jacket pocket; I learned how to undo the safety catch unobtrusively, with a flick, as if I were busy looking for extra papers or something. The necessity of having to fire with my left hand made me feel rather uneasy.

We traveled around the country a great deal, sometimes by train but mostly on bicycles; we went to all the market towns as well as the cities—to Venice, Verona, Treviso, Rovigo. Of course we avoided Vicenza, where everybody knew us. A couple of times I even went on my bicycle to Milan, the Center of Centers.

These trips were possible because of the support given to us by a large number of families and individuals. The real, professional helpers were undoubtedly few; but the assistance from these people was of incalculable value. They gave us hospitality, fed us, provided us with bicycles, delivered messages, kept deposits of arms and caches of letters and documents in their houses, even looked after our clandestine radio sets, not to mention the operators of our clandestine radio sets; and they were also ready to call in, if necessary, some trustworthy technician for these radios, or the family doctors for the operators.

We spent months liaising all over the Veneto. Many a time we were stopped because of the black market; but we only had seditious papers in our heavy fiber suitcases; they searched for butter and found *Justice and Liberty*. Those of us who were stopped used to maintain that we had lost the keys of our suitcases and while waiting for a decision to be made about whether or not the suitcases should be forced open, we looked around for the best way to escape. Then we escaped.

So, apart from everything else, these months were energetic ones; we did our escaping in towns and in the country. Sometimes we had to abandon our contraband, but at others we managed to take it with us, thus making our escaping all the more exhausting. Occasionally we had to get rid of some bicycles, but never, so far as I know, did we get rid of the money that we so often had to carry with us. A sign of our solid bourgeois upbringing.

We ran our worst risks of arrest through the false papers, the forged identity documents and military permits. There was no risk when they were first checked over, but when it was decided that we had to be taken off for a more thorough investigation, then the danger was very great: one false paper was like a small time bomb in one's pocket.

It never happened to me; but it often did happen to the others when they suddenly found themselves involved in a roundup, and had to sound plausible about the bogus illnesses specified on their medical history sheets. Bene had pleurisy in his right shoulder.

"Let me see it," said the lieutenant.

"You can't," said Bene. "It's inside."

From then onward every morning he painted his right shoulder, and even part of his back, with iodine.

A false permit in one's pocket, a parcel of newspapers on one's luggage rack, a beret on one's head to confound any acquaintances one might run into, and quite often a cache of thousand-lire notes. The newspapers circulated principally within the organization; they would be written, then printed, then delivered to the Center, and finally distributed throughout the countryside. And to whom? To those who had written, printed, transported, and distributed them. All these people read and studied them with great satisfaction; then they began writing once more, and it started all over again. At least that was the impression we had.

It was all a closed system. Like the million lire in Franco's long pants. We went about with millions of lire. We lived like ascetics, measuring out our food and all that sort of thing; if we wanted to buy a book we had to do without a meal; and the whole time we were carrying about maybe half a dozen millions at one go, hundreds of millions of lire in today's money. We carried them in a bag, or hidden on our persons. They were in thousand-lire notes, and I don't think we ever lost a single one. In the evening, when we arrived at houses belonging to families who were giving us hospitality, we would take out these sweaty and crumpled millions, and sometimes lay them out on the ground to dry. Most families had never seen a million all in one, in their whole lives; and with due caution we showed them these notes lying on the floor.

On one occasion the million in Franco's long pants stayed there for two entire days; at the beginning it rustled a great deal, then it settled down somewhat. The first evening, on a halt during his journey, Franco left it inside, because he was tired; the second evening when he arrived at his destination, he took the money out, and it happened that one of the thousand-lire notes had got stuck above his right knee, and had disintegrated. Franco was terrified. The people who were to have had it assured him that it didn't matter (I suppose they thought that the other nine hundred and ninety-nine would be ample); but he had no peace until he had recovered all the little bits scattered about the right leg of his pants; he stuck the note together, and later a banker-conspirator from Lonigo undertook to exchange it for a good one.

There were times when we felt as though we were ourselves the shadow government of the Veneto; at other times we felt exceedingly insignificant, just a handful of guys mooning around on bicycles. In theory we kept in touch with the *comitati*, the commands, and the political or military resistance groups of the various towns and villages; in practice we met only a few people, and the very nature of our encounters with them increased our feeling of unreality. It was all rather strange; one would say: "A week from today, we'll meet here at the same spot, at midday," and that was all. Once we agreed to meet at a crossroads in the country, at another time our rendezvous might be a stretch of road near a village, but more often than not we met by a bridge. Perhaps I exaggerate the importance we attached to bridges: nevertheless it did seem to me that we always tended to meet at these places. Often all I knew was the name of a bridge, perhaps in the depths of the country, and that someone would be there on some particular day of the week. As I rode toward this bridge on my bicycle, through the dry winter landscape, I would reflect to myself: One thing we must never ask is how many of us there really are. Then at last I would find the bridge, and there, leaning against the parapet and looking at the winter landscape, would be the subcommittee of Albettone, or—maybe—the headquarters of Monte Galdella—in actual fact one chap wearing an overcoat, and immersed in his own patriotic thoughts. We would liaise, exchange brief-cases, or the contents of brief-cases, and some political news; then I would leave. And so, from bridge to bridge, we did our resisting.

The *comitati* in the villages were on the basis of one representative for each political party; they were individuals with labels—little more than invisible badges—some of which were simply put on for the sake of symmetry. We've got the Communist, and the Socialist, and the Christian Democrat. . . . And you perhaps could be the Liberal, would you like to be the Liberal? And so the *comitato* will be complete.

Some of our political friends, who had been engaged in this work right from the beginning, were not yet resigned to the inevitability of having to cope with a large Catholic party at the end of the war. They tried to induce its representatives, occasionally quite open-minded people, to think it over.

"But do you have to have a party?" a friend of ours—active in a big market town—asked his Christian Democrat opposite number. "Why don't you Catholics allow yourselves to be spread, so to speak, among the other parties—the real ones—and then you could Christianize them?" (This was being a bit catty.) "Why do you want a party of your own, and to be in opposition to the others? You're only devaluing your faith and reducing it to the level of mere political merchandise." Then he concluded: "Come on, join the Action Party instead." The Christian Democratic listened, advanced only timid objections; but he didn't join that party.

Suddenly one day, they arrested him; and our friend, while being very sorry for him as a co-conspirator, rubbed his hands. "Politically, I'm pleased," he said. "The emphasis of the *comitato* has swung toward us." Nobody was unduly worried about these political arrests: after all, they hardly ever killed them in prison; so when someone went out of circulation, the rest of us would take a few extra precautions, and that would be that until we all met up again at the end of the war. However, some days afterward they also arrested our friend, so the emphasis of the *comitato* swung once more. They sent both to Dachau, where they certainly would have resumed their arguments about how best to arrange the future political structure of the country; but we don't know what transpired, because neither of them returned. This business of remaking Italy was a complicated thing.

Marietto and I, though based at the Center, liaised a lot. I think I rushed about on my bicycle more that winter than in all my bicycle training sessions in my entire life put together; all the same, our principal work was in the city too. Out of all our companions we were the only ones permanently in Padua; the others only came now and then. There were, however, a few girl-friends who stayed with us on the excuse of having to be at the University; and there was Simonetta, who was with us a great deal, so that soon she gave up both her studies and her family, much as we had done, and in effect did the same sort of job as we did.

I don't honestly remember now what precisely I was supposed to be. Military inspector? First Secretary of the Venetian Command? Commissar? I loathed the idea of having an official job, but I did have one nevertheless, and

I hope it was a little more important than Marietto's, if only for reasons of age. I lived in the same room with him; our tommy guns were in the wardrobe; under the bed we had the large suitcase containing the archives of the Regional Headquarters, with papers weighing scores of pounds inside. Its capture would have depopulated the entire region, but it had to be kept somewhere. I wonder now what this Regional Headquarters really was. It was an important institution, certainly, but I am not quite sure whether it was predominantly military or political; it was rather Kafkaish, essential but vague, almost inexistent. We worked, above all, for It, but without really knowing what It was; sometimes we had the idea It must have been in that large suitcase under the bed.

Besides being a Center, Padua also had its own local units. We called them the Gaps.* They were young men with whom we were continually in contact in the streets and cafés. Their duty was atrocious and fascinating: the proper answer to the shame and sinfulness of urban society—terrorism, pure and simple.

These youths were truly dynamic. Their expectation of life, especially as far as the leaders were concerned, was short enough: hardly a week passed without some of them dying in the streets, in bloodied raincoats.

One of them would fail to turn up at the appointed time. I would wait the prescribed number of minutes, then go away. Sometimes later a message would reach me during one of my many other appointments during the day. And when I went home in the evening, I would take out my *cahier jaune* and cross out the name and the time of the appointment with two or three tired pencil strokes, then I would tear out the page and light it with a match and watch it burn until the flame licked my finger.

Among our military superiors the one who was nearest

* G.A.P.: *Gruppi d'Azione Partigiana,* saboteur units.

to us, as well as being the most approachable, was Spartaco, a truly excellent fellow; he had only one favorite swear-word, brief and sorrowful, which could be written thus: *Coio.* He said it in a strident tone of voice, different to his normal one. He was from the Friuli. Politically speaking, we had no direct superiors, apart from the enormous moral authority of Franco, who—of all who did this liaising—was the most active. Being lame, Franco couldn't walk much, but he was marvelous with a bicycle; the bicycle was an integral part of his personality. Thus, in this cycling phase of the Resistance, in this kingdom of bicycles, Franco dominated. He had a real passion to inspire people, to promote things: he never wanted to keep his ideas or discoveries, valuable as they often were, to himself, but he had to share them, liberally, with others; even in peacetime he would always be rushing around spreading the honey of his political wisdom—an idea here, a reprimand there, a bibliography there.

In matters strictly political we trusted him absolutely. It is true that we also came in contact with various other sources of political thinking, incomparably more renowned: old anti-Fascists, learned professors, the people in fact to whom we usually went in order to get the editorials for our clandestine newspapers. But they didn't always seem really convincing to us. We did believe in a corpus of anti-Fascist knowledge, but we rejected the idea that these people were its custodians. If we could have induced Franco to play the political leader a bit, we would have felt more at ease: but he only wanted to be the inspiration, never the leader.

So Marietto and I, when we weren't coping with appointments and trips into the country and the *comitati*, had to study too, though not of course to take exams or anything like that. We literally studied for Italy, for the nonexistent great ruling class that had to emerge after the war. Had to.

It was cold that winter. We studied at the same table, wrapped in blankets, with woolen face masks on our heads and woolen gloves on our hands. We peered out of the slits in our masks at the grim landscape of Italian culture; we turned the pages laboriously with our gloved fingers.

We put ourselves through a quick course in anti-Fascist knowledge. When we opened the red *Quaderni di Giustizia e Libertà,* noblest of clandestine magazines, we had the feeling of drawing from an immense, almost sacred fountain. We tried to understand and absorb not only individual essays, but whole paragraphs, detached phrases, words. We believed that everything in these books signified knowledge and wisdom, even the commas. The misprints had a curious effect on us. We glimpsed a world of uncorrupted truth, a richness of which we had up to now been deprived.

We felt that we bore on our shoulders—had piled up on the table—the entire weight of the encyclopedia of political science. The story of the parties, the theory of the ruling classes, market economics, Italian agriculture, trade-unionism, Marxism, sociology: there was so much that it was our duty to tackle.

Sometimes personal doubts and anxieties assailed us. What would we do when the war was over, by way of a career, I used to ask myself? But I didn't say anything to Marietto, I didn't want to depress him. I thought sadly: I bet we'll just be historians of historiography.

In questions of immediate political importance we had the impression that it was up to us to take the initiative. The authorities whom we consulted in Padua seemed deaf, unresponsive, to our problems. Others, higher up, seemed unapproachable. When I went there in person, to the Center of Centers in Milan, on my bicycle, I was admitted into an antechamber—or was it perhaps the back room? It was full of illustrious people, looking very distinguished, arguing animatedly over a copy of the London *Times* which had just arrived. It seemed inconceivable that we could really interest them in our problems; we felt that we alone had to take full responsibility for them.

Civil war is too serious a thing, we said, to leave to impulse, to chance. We must introduce reason, we must control passion, meditate on the lessons of the past. We have got to be historically minded. We consulted Cuoco's *The Neapolitan Revolution,* in order to learn a little revolutionary wisdom, then we secretly produced a document which we hoped would help to keep the overenthusiastic in check when the moment came for the war to be over.

On the left-hand side of this document we listed military ranks and civil appointments, on the right we put down what punishment should be meted out. Italy, when we had done with her, was really going to be whittled down. Conscientiously we discussed each case:

"The captains, what about the captains? Death, or life imprisonment?"

"How many captains are there in Italy?"

We counted them up; then I said, sighing: "They'll have to be put to death, you know."

Marietto asked me how many men a captain commanded, and I told him; we weighed the pros and cons and finally wrote: "Death sentence: commuted."

We commuted punishments for many of our military offenders but rarely did it for civilians.

We felt it was vital to prevent any attempt at summary justice, that all unseemly passions should be kept in check. For the good of Italy, we thought, we must eliminate hatred from our hearts, allow reason to dominate.

"Don't you think it would be a good idea to kill their relatives too?"

For humanitarian and practical reasons, perhaps yes. One could draw up a table of consanguinity: the first grade would be shot without trial; the second would have the chance of asking to be shot. That would not only be the most humane way, but the safest: we had to do something about all this horror, this fratricidal chain reaction, we had to put an end to this trail of misery and bereavement.

Thus, in our little room, we worked out the problem of how to end the civil war. I realize now that our keenness had in a sort of way driven us mad. We were perfectly decent boys, honest and human; we had been good students, and came from honorable, hard-working, peaceable families. We were just suffering from an access of acute civil war madness, which nobody had diagnosed; it was like having jaundice for a week or two without knowing it, and one stays in bed with a fever, a kind of flu; and when one finally calls in the doctor, he says: "You've had jaundice."

Very carefully we drew up our lists of proscriptions, with a Summary of Proposals and Tables as appendices. When, years later, I read the *Modest Proposal* of Swift about making hungry Irish people eat their own children, I immediately saw that what we lacked was a sense of humor.

We hadn't any sense of humor, Marietto and I, as we huddled together muffled up and alone in our cold room— two philosophers, two historians, two budding Robespierres in a house in Padua. When the mind is buzzing with proposals such as ours, the best cure is to write them down. After we had sent our document to the Center, I felt much better. I was getting cured.

Marietto was taking off his socks, *calzinotti* he called them, using the Tuscan word. He was very young; he had barely left his family, in a sense; basically we all were like that, but he was even more so. He washed his face and neck, rubbing and rubbing them, as mothers used to make children do; he dressed, or undressed, dealt with his *calzinotti*, combed his hair, everything he did was just like a little boy; behind the Tuscan names he gave his clothes I sensed all the family scoldings that must have formed a pattern of behavior for him.

I suddenly thought that our proposals didn't really have anything to do with Italy, and said so.

"What else have they to do with, then?"

"I don't know," I said. "This room."

"Oh, for God's sake," said Marietto. "Don't talk rubbish."

"Think of the problem of the bodies," I said. "These bodies have a volume and a weight; instead, a line of ink weighs practically nothing, it has a surface, but no volume to speak of; and an idea has neither weight nor volume."

"But we decided it was necessary to shoot these people."

"Perhaps it's enough just to shoot them with ink."

"Oh, for God's sake," said Marietto; but the observation must have made an impression on him, and gradually we got used to the idea of their already having been virtually shot, and in fact we referred to them as *i giustiziati*—the executed ones—to one another.

They took Marietto away from me at the beginning of spring, and strangely it was a captain who actually arrested him. The immediate cause was the clandestine press, the one which we criticized because it seemed only to be read by its compilers and distributors. But instead they read it at police headquarters as well, and one of the editions was read by the Captain of the GNR * in Via San Francesco. Marietto had set off for Venice on his bicycle with a fat bundle on his luggage rack; we always tried to leave as soon as curfew was over, early in the morning. At the entrance of the GNR Headquarters there was the Captain; he too was an early riser. The road was still practically deserted; Marietto passed in front of the doorway, pedaling briskly. Maybe he had attempted the Fascist salute; the fact is that the package fell off the luggage rack and rolled right in front of the Captain. Marietto halted, crimson in the face, and the Captain kindly picked up the package; this last had come undone, and the Captain began to read.

The GNR Headquarters was next door to the Palazzo

* *Guardia Nazionale Repubblicana,* the Fascist militia in the civil war.

Giusti (the notorious "torture chamber"). They broke a few of Marietto's cartilages and some of his bones, that we do know, because at the end of the war when he came out these were still not mended; they did other things to him, but he never wanted to let us know the details. He only said to me, when he came out, that the female jailers spoke to the prisoners with extraordinary liberty.

Spring was beginning when Marietto was arrested. I reported what had happened to Spartaco, and he said: *"Coio."*

While he was in prison Marietto never said a word, so no further arrests were forthcoming, but in those first hours I was not to know if he would speak or indeed had spoken and if so whether the GNR would be waiting for me in our room—and in the meantime prying into our suitcase. Spartaco told me to send Simonetta ahead, and off she went to the room, in a reckless sort of way, whistling a tune. I waited under the arcades, with my bicycle at the ready. Nobody was there, so in a comple of shakes we had emptied the place, and we made off, wheeling the bicycle with the fiber suitcase across the handle bars, to look for other lodgings. There were several of us in Spartaco's brood knocking about Padua: André from Belluno, with his aristocratic features, Fiorò from Treviso, as big as a camel, the Prussian-looking Meo, and various others. The whole lot of us belonged to the Action Party, but I still hankered after our original band, the small group of my friends from Vicenza.

I thought: I must get back to the mountains. The previous year we had left in March, and now it was almost that. Our duty is up there, I thought, I don't want to go on looking after suitcases, and I don't want to be an urban terrorist, a member of the Gap; back to the mountains, I've had enough of towns and pavements. My friends had exactly the same instincts. Enrico sent me a message: "Up to the Cima Posta? Right?" and I sent a message back: "Yes." Maybe we would have turned into the perfect soldiers, up there on the bare peaks of the Cima Posta, if the war had gone on for another couple of months. But there was no time, we were (though we didn't know it) in the last weeks of the war. There were delays, some more arrests, and I had to make an urgent and long trip into the country. Two of us had in fact to go; I went with Simonetta.

We started our journey in front of the curious misshapen façade of Santa Sofia, where we had agreed to meet. It was morning. Simonetta was in a smart sports outfit. She had a beautiful, lightweight woman's bicycle, with shining aluminum wheels, and the way she rode this bicycle was—one might say—the quintessence of sportive grace. It was a way invented by her; later it spread throughout Italy, and the people who have an eye for such things associate it, I believe, with the Italian girls of the period after the war. The English girls, immediately after the war, rode their bicycles in quite a different way. They were pretty too; but the other method, the Italian one, was incomparably more modern. Simonetta had invented it.

We were away for perhaps a week, in the district around Padua, Verona, and Vicenza. We traveled along secondary roads, with hard snow on the verges, and icy surfaces. For the most part, we slept together, I mean in the same place, sometimes in houses, sometimes in haylofts—but always with the permission of the owners. I don't remember where or how we ate; certainly, in secret, we drew on the resources of each other's youth, at least I think I was principally nourished by her vivacious little figure, her gray sweaters, her skirts with the sporting cut, her face without lipstick. I never dreamed of making love to her. She undressed, when we went to sleep, even when we had our bed in the straw; I turned the other way until she was undressed, chattering away to her the while. When we were lying down close to one another, I would go on talking a little more, and she for the most part would be silent, and then we would say to one another: *"Dormi bene,* sleep well," and off we would go to sleep.

She must be the prettiest partisan of the century, I

thought; certainly the most elegant. If I woke up first in the morning, and found myself next to her, it would give me quite a start. I would look at her sleeping—so serene, so pretty, lying so sweetly in the straw. How strangely things emerge from other things, I thought: the corn is cut, the straw gathered in, children are raised, wars are begun, a hundred currents cross one another, and then suddenly we have Simonetta, in this war, here on this straw.

I stood watching her until she opened her eyes, and she gave her first little smile, and said: *"Ciao,"* and I said: *"Ciao,"* and another day began.

On the penultimate evening of our tour we stopped at Marta's house in the country. Marta was in prison, or already at the hospital, I don't remember which; because she was transferred directly to hospital, from the prison, where they did whatever they did to her, those ugly brutes. The house was empty and silent. There was a fauna of various refugees in the lower rooms: a family that had been bombed out, an old Jewish lady—I think that the peasants fed them. We kept the shutters closed and the lights lowered so that they would not be seen down the valley. The house was comfortable; there was almost a feeling of luxury after our wanderings. We were there on the divan bed in the studio, with these lowered lights, and all the sleeping books around us. Simonetta was dressed as for the city; I don't know how she had these clothes, but at the right moment she always did have them. We were lying on this divan, talking idly. Then she decided she wanted to listen to some music; there were a phonograph and some records, and so we listened to sonatas and fugues and the like, and it seemed to me that they meant a great deal to her. The music was far from worrying me, the volume was very low, there was this thin thread of sound that one could almost pick up with two fingers, so to speak. When the evening was a little further advanced, the time came to go to bed; I on the divan, and Simonetta in another room. It was like that: a moment came when she got up and said, "Good night, then," and I said, "Good night," and she went into the other room.

Our journey along those icy roads was over. We separated the next day, in the country to the northeast of Vicenza, at the end of the afternoon; there was a long straight road which went into another at right angles. Narrow roads, covered with snow. We went on very slowly, talking of how women get on with men, and vice versa. The dry snow crunched under the tires. We stopped to finish our talk at the crossroads. There was nobody around.

"I think it's all a myth," I said, "that at a given moment, in this business of love, one really finds what one is looking for."

Simonetta said I was wrong, it was true, she had found it these past days. Then she got on her bicycle again and said: "*Ciao,*" and away she went, with that elegant way she had.

When she had gone I thought: Well, well. Instead of going up into the mountains with Enrico, I seem to be stealing his girl down here in the plain.

She could cycle very fast, too. I was more or less a racing cyclist (I mean I had been one, like every self-respecting Italian boy) and had gone through proper training sessions and so on, but honestly there were times during this journey when I had to go all out to keep up with her.

I remember that farewell on the snowy road very vividly. We were separated for several days. What came afterward, I remember rather less well. I still remember how her eyes looked when you peered into them very closely; they weren't what you would normally call beautiful eyes, eyes that people compare to flowers, or stars; they were any eyes, somewhere between green and gray I would say—young, quite attractive. But when you looked at them closely, you discovered something very special about them; they were full of all sorts of colors, like a lovely miniature garden, into which I seemed to enter.

11

RAIN IN THE morning, a feeling of exaltation; Simonetta in the electric air, with her pearl-gray sweater and tommy gun slung over her shoulder. The insurrection of Padua was quite an event, something we happily improvised that spring. We were out in the streets—armed, excited, young. The war was ending in a spate of brave deeds. Yet I must confess that she seemed the most important thing of all to me—her figure was so full of grace, her face looked so serious because of this insurrection.

Spartaco's brood was dispersed throughout the city, fostering the insurrection and, subsequently, trying to run it. Lots of people were beginning to get busy. The grandest of them had gathered at the Jesuit Fathers' building; they were assembled in the entrance hall, in groups, arguing. From the street outside the building we could see as far as the Pra della Valle; a car had stopped in the middle of the paved street, a wall on one side and arcades on the other; groups of partisans were lolling about; then suddenly—as in a joke—

shells began to explode all around us. I recognized a 20-millimeter machine gun, from the sound of the bullets tearing into the body of the car; the Germans were firing from the Pra della Valle, enfilading the whole street. There probably was about a platoon of them; every now and then we saw a German helmet under the arches at the far end of the Pra. We too began to fire, from behind the pillars, in groups of twos and threes. We might have been shooting peas from a catapult. The machine gun was sweeping the street authoritatively; the car was in flames.

I tried to ease myself a little farther forward to get closer to the machine gun; others were doing the same; things were ricocheting all over the place in the arcade. I got past two pillars, and at the third there was a boy seated on the ground, leaning against the pillar. He was dressed in civilian clothes and was about my age. A patch of scarlet blood had formed on his shoulder; instinctively I looked to see if there were drops on the pavement, but as yet there weren't any. I saw at once that he wasn't afraid; for some seconds I stood there watching him, and I thought: This is pure 1848.

I slung my tommy gun around my neck, and the one belonging to the wounded boy too; then I took him by his good shoulder and dragged him under the arcade. There was a typically Paduan doorway, the sort that looks as though it belongs to a deserted house; I saw a bell without a name, and rang it.

The Paduan door gave a little click and opened. Inside there was a huge, empty hall, a staircase. We were going up this staircase, the wounded boy and I; I held on to him by his waist, he had put his free arm round my neck, we were managing quite well. I asked myself: I wonder if he is making them now, the drops, on the stairs? but I couldn't turn around to look. Halfway up the staircase he remembered his tommy gun, and stopped. I told him that I'd got it. Then I looked up the staircase, and thought: This is really going too far. Two blonde, pretty girls had appeared out of the door and were already coming down the first steps, their arms amorously extended. I felt as though I had fallen inside a book. The pleasure was overwhelming.

Later we were in a room with high windows, very Paduan, facing a tired, tranquil garden. The wounded boy was seated on a bed, his torso naked, and the girls were busying themselves around him. One of the girls, the more attractive of the two, was dressed as a nurse; she had ash-blonde hair and was bandaging his shoulder with snow-white gauze bandages. She told us that she studied law at the University but had also taken Red Cross courses, and obviously she had her white uniform with a scarlet cross ready to hand. Perhaps she too thought: There'll never be an occasion like this again.

The Red Cross girl showed me out and stopped at the top of the stairs. At the foot I turned to wave to her; she smiled at me and I saw what she was really like: virginal, neat, blonde, a little on the thin side, and very sweet. I felt untidy and dirty, overexcited, dark. I blew a kiss, and gracefully she returned it.

Down below, the shooting continued; every now and then the Germans at the far end of the Pra sprayed the street with great masses—sackfuls—of machine-gun bullets. Even if there are only a dozen of them, I thought, and they want to attack us, what is there to prevent them? After all, they've had five years' practice; one street more or less hardly counts. They'll go into the Jesuits' building, and they'll murder all the bigwigs in there arguing about who is going to make the first speech to the citizens of Padua; and then perhaps they'll murder the Jesuits too. The whole lot almost deserve it, bloody fools.

I felt that I ought at least to go and warn these people, so I rushed into the building. When I came into the hall the spectacle of all of them jabbering away among the Jesuits made me lose my head, and I began to shout like a man possessed. That densely packed assembly fell silent; the

263

sound of my rage infuriated me all the more, and without really meaning it I began yelling and swearing at the top of my voice, every now and then interpolating the most terrible oaths between my pieces of communication. I don't know if, in the entire history of the Institute, such oaths had ever been heard so loudly, in that room. The people in there listened to me without protest, and I must confess without much interest. Then they turned around once more, to form their groups, and began jabbering away again.

I went back to the arcade, extremely irritated. We've even got to protect the fools of this world, I said to myself. There were still two or three of us under the arcade. We darted in zigzags among the pillars, getting rid of a few bullets just to show that we were there. One of the others got a piece of shrapnel in his leg, so he mixed his bullets with a few obscenities. When the Germans decided to come out I thought: Here goes; now for the grenades: not that they'll have any effect. But strangely the Germans—a group of gentlemen in green—had raised their hands and kept them up. Mària-Vergine! * I'd never seen them like this, I was almost frightened. I saw a collection of armed civilians rushing across the Pra; I ran out and was just in time to shout: Here, take these, can't wait, before they engulfed them of their own free will. I didn't get involved in any other specially large shooting affray after that, though there were a few isolated machine-gun bursts directed at me from windows and attics, usually at a street turning, and I would retaliate. They did no harm to me, and I suppose I did none to them, so we were quits. The war was over, but we were not yet aware of it.

Suddenly there was a kind of carnival atmosphere. People, running, walking, marching; people appearing from everywhere, mostly wearing tricolor armbands. But who on earth can they be? I asked myself. If there was a burst of fire at a

* The author claims that the stress *Mària* is essential.

street corner, they would disappear, and two or three of us would carry on with our game among the pillars; then the carnival began again.

My friends and I were busy; now and then we'd bump into each other in the street, each of us intent on his own business. We collected weapons, prisoners. Then I caught sight of Simonetta's back; she was accompanying an enormous German, who had on an enormous black leather overcoat, and a helmet in proportion. She was looking as pretty as ever, with the tommy gun over her shoulder and that pearl-gray sweater, the same color as the sky. The German looked like a great black blot beside her. They were ten yards away from me, and between us was all the hullabaloo of the carnival; I shouted to her as loud as I could, and she heard me and they both turned around together. The German was our friend Fiorò. Soon we shall all be indistinguishable, I thought: friends and enemies. They waved to me, he was smiling, happy as anything, she had that little insurrectionary pout which she had put on that morning, and she looked marvelous. Then they went around the corner and the carnival separated us. Things changed minute by minute.

This can't be an important insurrection, I thought, but in its own little way it certainly is a good example of how insurrections work. The forces about us are impersonal ones, they change continually, like eddies in a swift river. There doesn't seem to be any proper central point, yet centers are constantly forming; if you manage to find yourself in one of these centers, you are at once in complete control of the situation without having to do a thing. I realized that this was the art of being a revolutionary: you must keep your eyes forever open, be ready for that current, know how to recognize a center when you're in it and eddies as they approach you.

There are two alternatives: either you have your revolutionary program worked out already, or you have an instinct for it—and that, without any doubt, is something rare.

265

I considered my own program: it was not ready; I looked at my instinct, and it didn't seem very rare to me. What a ridiculous situation, I thought: to have learned how to do it, but not to know what to do.

Every now and then I found myself with a group of really reliable people—genuine Gap boys obviously, even if they weren't wearing armbands; I got them to do some minor winkling out, and various other rather unimportant jobs. What a waste, I said to myself, not to use them for something big; with all that there is to do in Italy, not to mention the certainty that if some things aren't done today they can never be done tomorrow, and God knows if they'll ever be done—when we are old graybeards no doubt, and then they won't matter. We just aren't ready. Padua at this stage belongs to anybody who wants her; it must be the same with the whole of northern Italy: within a few hours, at the most within a few days, we must hand her back. Wouldn't it at least be worth our while doing something useful, however little, however unsystematic? A little thinning out of the upper middle class, for instance, or the ecclesiastical hierarchy?

Poor *signori*, secular and ecclesiastic, maybe they were all very nice people. And most likely full of good will toward us. But to me, then, they belonged to categories which I considered to be generically harmful to Italy. So they were running into this danger, in my mind that is; I decided to do nothing.

Things kept changing; friends of mine were beginning to arrive with camouflaged vehicles, trucks, exotic uniforms, leather overcoats, helmets. Processions, cortèges began; crowds of people with armbands marched resolutely along, some singing, some waving objects of various sorts. Flags appeared at windows; the ones with the royal arms on them annoyed me; the ones without appeared odd, like putting on a vest the wrong way round. For a moment I had an absurd desire to retire at once from the whole affair, to go to the university library that very morning, take out a book, and begin studying. Apart from the fact that the library would have been closed.

We began to converge on certain palaces and halls. On one was written *Comando*, on another *Direzione*, on another *Partito*, and on another *Comitato*. Some of us clustered at the entrances, some sat inside behind tables. There was a great coming and going. In the rooms of the palaces were important people who had got committees started. I was with Marietto now. During the morning he had been let out of prison, along with thieves and other political prisoners; Marietto had met me in the street, like a ghost in full daylight, alive and well except for those broken things which weren't visible.

We found ourselves in the *salone* of an important palace, and from a shiny dark door there appeared a rather authoritative-looking man (actually a friend of ours, older than we were and one of our immediate superiors). He saw us and called out:

"The leading article in tomorrow morning's newspaper. The first free newspaper of the Veneto. You both write it. Quick."

Marietto began swallowing hard. I asked: "What do you want us to say in this article?"

"That's for you to decide."

"Marietto and I aren't educated," I said.

"What?"

"We're uneducated, politically uneducated. We've nothing to say. We can't educate ourselves by writing at the expense of the public. This is something for somebody who's more mature."

Instead of being annoyed the man became sad.

"How can you say such a thing at a moment like this?" he murmured.

"We must study, not write articles," I said. "We've already

written our articles in the Fascist newspapers, at least I have, he hasn't because he was too young."

His face said: "How sad!" His eyes were so disappointed, they searched the room for something that was not quite so painful. Near us was Zaccheo, dark, excited, bespectacled.

"You," said the man.

Zaccheo clicked his heels proudly. He wore a German helmet.

"Do you feel like writing the leading article for tomorrow's newspaper?"

"At your command," said Zaccheo, clicking his heels again. Sense of responsibility oozed from him. The authoritative-looking man gave him some orders, then some paper; then he went back, into the heart of that important palace. Zaccheo, with the helmet on his head, began to write.

His first name I no longer remember, still less his surname: his face I also forget. I do remember the color of his hair, something between blond and brown, his way of looking at one and his general build, which was large and strong. The boy exists no more, only these fragments of memory are left in my mind.

I was seated at a table dealing with various emergency matters; I felt full of a sense of urgency and uselessness. The floor was large and gleaming. Someone came up to my table, stood at attention, and said:

"Those three that were killed, at Voltabarozzo, they've been put in the chapel there. Here are their wallets."

When I took out the first identity card, it was he who looked at me.

I don't even remember much about my relationship with this boy; I remember the general shape of my feelings—that I was fond of him, felt a certain admiration as well as protectiveness, such as a slightly more introverted man would feel toward a slightly younger one.

I raised my eyes and said to the messenger:

"But this man is dead?"

I got up and walked toward the window meaning to look out. But when one feels grief such as this, it's easier to look downward, look at the floor. On the floor there was an arrangement of glistening squares.

Half an hour later Zaccheo and I entered the room where a group of men were doing committee work around a table. I tried to open my mouth, but all I did was to stand there at attention, looking at these people doing their committee work. Zaccheo took over, completely under control. He held the German helmet under his arm, jumped to attention, and announced in a firm, precise voice:

"I have to inform the committee that the commander of the Paduan *gruppi d'azione* fell in battle this morning at Voltabarozzo."

Eyes glinted behind pince-nez. The men around the table took heed of the news with due discretion; they seemed to be saying: "Good, good; good boys." Then they returned to the problem of printing manifestoes.

In the evening I went in a truck to take the three bodies away. They had been put on the chapel floor, and the principal impression I had was that they looked so clumsy in their clothes. The faces were pallid and seemed like old wax. I felt much better. The truth is really this, I thought; grief ultimately is connected with truth. We put these clumsy-looking boys on the truck and returned to Padua, and that was the end of it.

I went personally to meet the Allied Eighth Army when it finally made up its mind to enter Padua. I was on a patrol between the Santo and the Bassanello, a little before midnight. Curious scenes occurred at the roadblocks. The passwords were all different, and strictly speaking we ought to have been firing at one another every thirty yards; only the sense of general euphoria I believe prevented a universal slaughter. They say that euphoria usually makes people start firing; but it doesn't make them aim straight.

I had passed the last roadblock, with my patrol (Simonetta was with us, with her tommy gun), and we walked into the deep dark on the periphery of the town, down a long road between houses and heading south from Padua. Naturally nobody was on the road; I knew that the Allies were close, but German units were continually passing nearby. This, then, is how a war ends, I said to myself. First an army leaves, then another arrives. Yet it's not really the end. The war ends in people's minds, it happens a little earlier for some than it does for others; this is why there are still these senseless shootings.

At the far end of the main road we heard the groaning of powerful motors; it was something compact, intense.

"The British," I said to Simonetta, just for luck, for I was wondering what the odds were against its being the last German column. I decided less than 30 per cent.

"Are you sure it's the British?" she asked.

"Absolutely sure," I said, and she murmured: "It's like a dream."

In fact it did literally seem like a dream. We had been waiting only two years, but now it seemed much, much longer.

We walked down the middle of the road, going toward the Eighth Army, or at least 70 per cent of it, but I didn't worry about percentages any more. The noise became louder, and we felt smaller and smaller, in the middle of that dark road. Confusedly we began to distinguish the dark shapes of tanks: they were enormous. When we were fifty yards away I made the patrol stop; we had two flashlights, and I began to make signals. Then I went ahead a little, with Simonetta.

How strange life is, I thought. The British have arrived. Welcome. These tanks are our allies. With their hunched backs, their vast armored plating, their guns. They want what we want. Europe is full of these enormous allies of ours; how insignificant we must seem from the top of one of those tanks! Just people in rags; bands. Bandits. Foreigners have always thought of Italy as being a land of bandits.

The first tank stopped; there was an officer up on top with a soldier. I would have liked to say something historic, but I was feeling a bit emotional.

"You aren't Germans then?" I asked.

"*Not really,*" said the officer, in English.

"Welcome," I said. "The city is already ours."

"May we come up?" asked Simonetta, impulsive as ever. Now the patrol didn't matter any longer; we heard the column beginning to pile up behind the first tank, for hundreds and hundreds of yards; the rumbling of the engines was magnificent. So we re-entered the city, sitting on a tank and shouting at the British.

"And who are you?" said the officer after a bit.

"Fucking bandits," I replied without thinking. But suddenly I realized I shouldn't say such things in front of Simonetta, and I blushed; however, it was dark, and no one noticed. The officer shouted: "*I beg your pardon?*" and I shouted back: "I said we are Freedom Volunteers."

"Freedom?" shouted back the officer, and I confirmed this.

Then I added: "Now I'll sing a song. About you. Do you mind?"

"Sing away," he said, so I started:

> *Years have passed,*
> *Months have passed,*
> *The English are here*
> *At last, at last.*

Simonetta joined in the refrain. I'm always out of tune, but she never is; at any rate the uproar drowned everything.

> *Our country is the world entire,*
> *Our faith is liberty.*
> *Our only thought—to save humanity!*

"What do those words mean?" asked the officer.

"That the war is over," I said. Then I added: "And that what interests us most is the salvation of humanity."

"You a poet?" asked the officer, with some suspicion.

I put my hand around his ear and shouted: *"Just a fucking bandit."*

Thus we entered Padua with the Eighth Army, then Simonetta and I went to sleep, and we left them there between Piazza Cavour and Piazza Garibaldi.